THE BOYS' BOOK OF
RADIO, TELEVISION
AND
RADAR

ALSO IN THIS SERIES:

FOR YOUR SISTER:

THE BOYS' BOOK OF
RADIO, TELEVISION
AND
RADAR

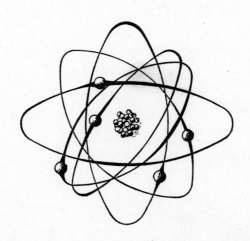

BURKE ★ LONDON

Burke Publishing Co. Ltd.
55 Britton Street, London, E.C.1.
Printed in Great Britain by
C. Tinling & Co. Ltd., Liverpool, London and Prescot.

CONTENTS

ACKNOWLEDGEMENTS

The Publishers wish to thank the following for permission to reproduce photographs and drawings:

The Air Ministry
The British Broadcasting Corporation
Central Electricity Authority
Dawe Instruments Ltd.
Decca Radar Ltd.
De Havilland Propellers Ltd.
E.M.I. Ltd.
H.M. Stationery Office
Marconi Ltd.
The Metal Box Co. Ltd.
Mullard Ltd.
The Postmaster-General
Pye Ltd.
J. Arthur Rank Ltd.

CHAPTER I

THE ELECTRON
CREATES A NEW SCIENCE

OUR STORY commences in 1879; the place is an inventor's laboratory in America. His name was Thomas Alva Edison, and to him we owe amongst other things the modern telegraph and the gramophone. In the year mentioned, however, Edison was experimenting with one of the first electric lamps whose invention he shared with Swan in this country. The lamp consisted of a short filament of carbon enclosed in a bulb from which as much air as possible had been extracted, wire connections to the two ends of the filament being sealed through the glass and linked to the terminals of an electric battery. The current from the latter, in overcoming the resistance of the carbon filament, raised it to a white heat.

However, for a reason quite unconnected with the matter I wish to introduce here, Edison had also inserted in one of his bulbs a thin plate of metal (Figure 1), a connection to this also running through the glass to the outside, and, lo and behold, he found that if the plate connection was joined to the *positive* pole of his battery, a small current could be detected flowing between filament and plate, just as though there existed a real electric "circuit". Incidentally, if the plate was joined to the other (negative) pole, no current could be observed.

This was really a startling and unheard-of proceeding. That a current could flow round a circuit with a large *gap* in it could not be explained at all in those days. It had long been known, of course, that if a very large charge of electricity could be built up by means of a Leyden jar, a Wimshurst machine or a Rhumkorff induction coil, it was capable of jumping an air gap in the form of a spark, but otherwise it had always been assumed that, for electricity to "flow" some sort of conductor, either a solid one like a copper, or a liquid "electrolyte", was necessary.

But here Edison had a current flowing from one side of a gap in a metallic conductor to the other without any fuss and with no visible means of support at all, for, as you will remember, most of the air had been extracted from the bulb. Unfortunately, Edison, genius though he was, failed completely to see what this really meant, and how momentous and startling his discovery was. So he just recorded his observations, and the experiment has been known ever since as the "Edison Effect", but on the simple fact that, under certain conditions, a current of electricity can flow *in space*, an entirely new science has been born. We now call this new science "electronics", and to it we owe some of the most important as well as most interesting scientific developments of modern times.

With the aid of these currents in space men's powers have been immeasurably extended. They can talk to others many thousands of miles away without wires and they can see things out of sight. They can hear sounds previously unheard. They can heat without heat. They can with radar guide ships unerringly through treacherous channels in the thickest fog and, by the aid of the electron microscope, photograph things too small to be seen by ordinary light even with the most powerful microscopes.

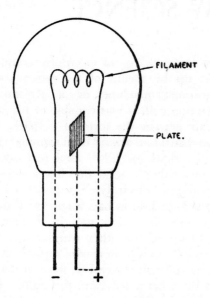

FIGURE I. *Thomas Edison had inserted in the bulb a plate of thin metal with a wire running through the base to the outside, and when this wire was joined to the positive terminal of the same battery that fed the lamp, a small current could be detected flowing through the vacuum within the bulb from the filament to the plate.*

What the Electron can do?

Electronic devices can count more rapidly than the cleverest human, and they make no mistakes. They can weigh, measure and check; open or close valves; reject objects from conveyor belts; cut off the flow of materials. They can operate motors that open doors, move elevators, conveyors or cars, turn machinery and change the setting of valves and handles. They can control the thickness of plates and coatings, their temperatures, pressure, position and colour. And they can do all these things automatically, without human supervision.

Yet we have only touched upon the fringe of their uses up to now. If you can visualise a measuring tape one mile long as the possible field for the application of electronic devices, what has been done so far would probably take up no more of this distance than a halfpenny.

This book is largely the story of the rise of this new science of electronics, some of whose most fascinating applications I shall introduce to you in later chapters. First, however, we have to know a little more about the why and wherefore of those strange "currents in space" which first revealed themselves to Edison, for in them men eventually discovered the "secret of the electron".

How Cathode Rays are Produced

This brings us to that phenomenon known as the "cathode rays", which are really only another form of the "currents in space".

In its normal state, air or any other gas is not a good conductor of electricity. If the wire connecting the two poles of a battery is cut, the current ceases to flow in the wire because it cannot pass the tiny air gap thus created. But if the electric tension is made great enough, the insulating power of the air is broken down and a spark passes.

The passage of a current over a gap in a powerful electric circuit is, however, made much easier if the pressure of the air or other gas filling the gap is reduced, and in the 70's and 80's of last century the passage (or "discharge") of electricity through rarefied gases was much investigated, probably because the discharges are generally luminous and accompanied by often beautiful colour effects.

Amongst the effects to be discovered as men were able to extract more and more gas from their tubes were the "cathode rays". They are produced as follows:

The discharge tube (Figure 2) is about 12 centimetres long by 3 centimetres in diameter, and has a connection leading to a vacuum pump. Two aluminium plates A and C form the "electrodes". Plate A, called the "anode", is connected to the positive terminal of an induction coil, whilst plate C, called the "cathode", is connected to the negative terminal. When working, the induction coil supplies a high-tension current of several thousand volts in one direction only.

Suppose we set both pump and coil in operation. As the pressure is reduced, violet sparks are seen to flash across the tube between the plates. Then the dis-

It is separated from the blue negative glow by a dark space called the "Faraday dark space", whilst a narrow gap called the "Crookes dark space" can just be observed between the negative glow and the cathode.

Cathode Rays appear only when all Air is removed

Much lower pressures in the tube are required, however, for the production of cathode rays, so that it is natural that they were not observed until vacuum pumps had been considerably improved. If we continued pumping with a good pump we should find that the positive column

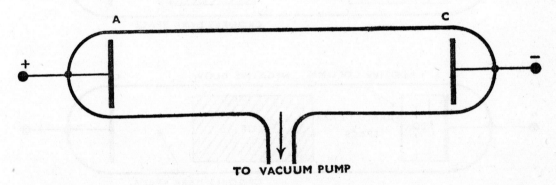

FIGURE 2. *Vacuum discharge tube that evolved from Edison's discovery. When plates A and C (anode and cathode) are connected to the positive and negative terminals respectively of an induction coil, currents flow along the tube with surprisingly beautiful colour effects. These, in their final form, are the cathode rays.*

charge gradually becomes steadier, changes to an orange-red, and broadens out, whilst a blue glow remains round the cathode. When pressure becomes as low as 1 or 2 millimetres of mercury (760 millimetres is normal atmospheric pressure) the luminous column broadens out and fills nearly the whole width of the tube, which will then appear much as in Figure 3 (*a*).

The uniform red luminous column extends for several centimetres from the anode, and is called the "positive column".

shortened and broken up into *striations*, that is, parallel streaks, whilst the Crookes dark space lengthened and the negative glow extended further along the tube (Figure 3 (*b*) and (*c*)).

If pressure is reduced still further, the positive column continues to shrink whilst the negative glow moves towards the anode and the Crookes dark space goes on expanding until eventually it fills the whole of the tube. During the later stages of pumping the glass is observed to glow with a greenish fluorescence and blue streamers

9

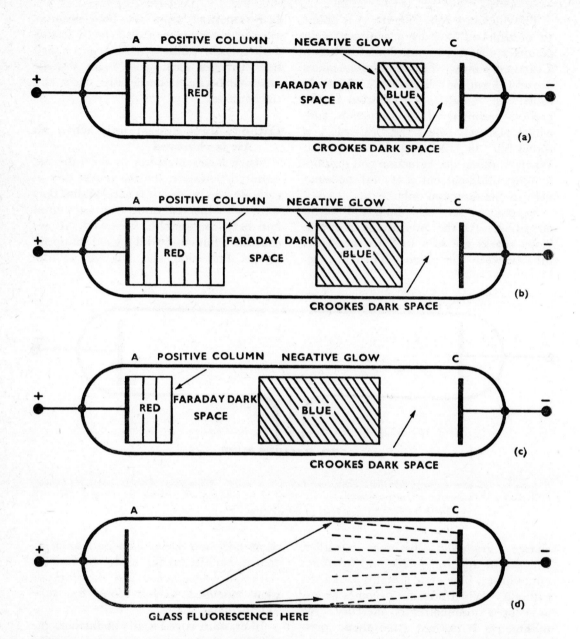

FIGURE 3. *Main phases through which the discharge passes as more and more air is withdrawn from the vacuum discharge tube.*

While there is still some air in the tube (a) violet sparks flash along it between the plates, but these gradually become steadier and turn orange-red in colour while a blue glow appears round the cathode.

The blue glow then becomes larger and the red smaller (b) and (c) until the blue glow moves towards the anode and the Crookes Dark Space fills nearly the whole tube. When the vacuum is complete, we see the real cathode rays (d) and their fluorescent effect on suitably coated glass.

or blue light rays seem to leave the cathode. These are the cathode rays, as they were first called, and the fluorescence is due to the rays hitting the glass (Figure 3 (d)).

These "rays", however, have two peculiar properties which distinguish them completely from any ordinary light rays. In the first place they can be *deflected*, i.e. turned from their path, by an electric or magnetic field, a thing quite impossible with light; and in the second place they can be led out from the tube through a thin pane of aluminium which would completely stop ordinary light, and they cause the air to glow for a short distance from it.

Now, whatever the gas originally in the tube, the same cathode rays are obtained; and the same rays are also obtained whatever the material from which the cathode is made.

These facts led to the conclusion that the cathode rays were not really "rays" in the

they were particles, had to be extremely small, much smaller than atoms, for it seemed quite unlikely that they could otherwise pass through a sheet of solid metal without leaving any trace.

Here it was, then, that a Professor (later Sir) J. J. Thomson stepped in with a series of momentous and extremely beautiful experiments by which he not only proved that the cathode rays evidently did consist of small particles carrying a negative charge, but also measured the strength of the charge relative to the size or mass of the particles. Not only did he prove that the charge and the mass were always the same, about 1/2000th of the mass of a hydrogen atom, whatever the gas in the tube and whatever the material from which the cathode was made, but he also proved that the particles could be produced in other ways and must form part of every atom.

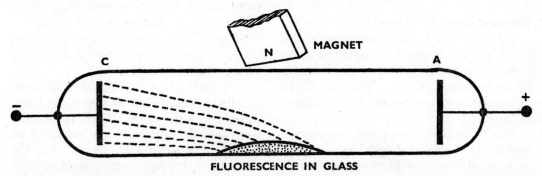

FIGURE 4. *Deflection of cathode rays by ordinary bar magnet shows that the discharge behaves as a collection of negatively charged particles of electricity. The direction in which the rays are deflected depends mainly on their speed, and in practice they form themselves into a spiral with right- or left-hand motion.*

normal sense of the word, but were streams of tiny particles of some sort. These particles, moreover, because they were deflected from their course by a magnet or by an electric field, must carry an electric charge (Figure 4). This charge had to be a *negative* one because the deflection followed certain rules as to direction which are well known even in elementary physics. Finally, the particles, if

Atom not the Smallest Particle

Everything, therefore, pointed to the fact that, in view of the size of the charge carried being so great in relation to the infinitesimally small mass of the particles, we were here in the presence of nothing more or less than little units of negative electricity. Not only that, but these particles were evidently part and parcel of any kind of matter, and the fact that they were considerably smaller than the lightest atoms spelled death to the idea which had ruled all physics and chemistry up till then: the idea that the atom was the smallest particle of matter which could exist.

Consequently, there followed from J. J. Thomson's work a revolution in science. In the first place, the flow of electricity, constituting an electric current, was now seen to be a flow of small particles which somehow entered into the composition of any type of matter. Each of these particles bore a negative charge, so that it would be attracted to any positively charged body. In the second place the atom was no longer the tiny solid, indivisible ball it had been regarded as; it was itself composed of smaller particles, some at least of which were the "electrons", as the cathode ray particles came to be called.

Elements and Compounds

We must now have a closer look at the atom, and we can best do so, perhaps, by remembering that all substances can be divided into two classes. They are either "elements" or "compounds" or mixtures of these.

For all practical purposes, no matter how finely you divided up a piece of gold, or lead, or iron, the particles would still be gold or lead or iron: but if you divided up a grain of salt sufficiently finely a time would come when any further division of your particles would result in splitting the salt into something that was no longer salt, but its two components, sodium and chlorine. Gold, lead, iron, sodium and chlorine are elements. Salt and most other familiar substances are compounds, consisting of two or more elements linked together.

The smallest particle that can exist, where elements are concerned, is an atom

of the element. The smallest particle of a compound that can exist and yet remain a compound, is a *molecule*. A molecule consists of two or more atoms linked together. For instance, if we wished to draw a picture of a molecule of salt, which is a compound of one sodium atom (chemical symbol Na) and one chlorine atom (chemical symbol Cl) we should have to make a drawing using signs or symbols something like those shown in Figure 5, below; whilst if we wanted to represent diagrammatically a molecule of water (H_2O), which consists of two hydrogen atoms (chemical symbol H) linked to a single oxygen atom (chemical symbol O), we should have something like that shown in Figure 6, although our diagram would bear no resemblance to a real molecule.

Now in view of the exceedingly small size of the atom you might think it would be impossible to find out even roughly how it was built up, but you would be wrong.

Suppose we wanted to know something about a dark cave before entering it. What would you suggest?

Perhaps the best idea would be to throw in a few stones. First we throw one hard, straight into the cave. Then, if the cave were very deep it would go bounding on and on and we should lose it. On the other hand, it might come bounding back almost immediately, but that would not necessarily prove the cave a shallow one,

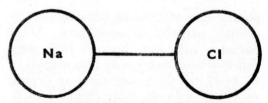

FIGURE 5. *Molecule of ordinary salt, consisting of one atom of sodium (Na) joined to one atom of chlorine (Cl). The circle and the line joining them are used here merely to indicate the number of atoms in the molecule. They do not indicate its shape.*

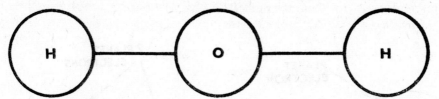

FIGURE 6. *Molecule of water, built up from two atoms of hydrogen (H) and one atom of oxygen. This is more complex in type than the molecule of salt. The linking lines indicate the assumed "bonds" or "lines of force" that join the atoms to form a molecule.*

for our stone might have struck an obstruction in the middle of it. We could soon prove this, however, by sending in stones at small angles to the centre and observing what happens.

This, very roughly, is one of the methods the scientists adopt in exploring the atom. They fire small missiles—fast-moving protons, neutrons and other particles—at it. Then, from the behaviour of the missile and the atom when they collide, the structure of the atom can be worked out.

We find that the inside of the atom is mostly space, and that it is something like our solar system. Most of its weight is concentrated at the centre, in what is called the nucleus. The nucleus corresponds to the sun. Round the nucleus revolve a number of electrons. In the lightest element, hydrogen, there is only one electron. In the heaviest naturally-occurring one, uranium, there are 92. Each different element has a different number of electrons revolving round the nucleus. Figure 7 shows some models of simple atoms.

Now about the inside of the atom being mostly space. First, how big is an atom? The scientist, who must be exact, would tell you that the diameter of an atom ranged from 0·0000000001 to 0·0000000002 of a metre, but that does not mean very much to us. Let me illustrate the smallness of the atom in another way, by showing how many there are in, say, a glass of water. Suppose we could label each of the molecules in our glass of water, every one, of course, containing three atoms, then pour the contents into the ocean and stir the latter thoroughly so as to distribute the marked molecules uniformly throughout the seven seas. If you then took a glass of water anywhere out of the ocean, you would find in it about a hundred of your marked molecules.

How Protons balance Electrons

Now let me give you an example to illustrate the scale of distances inside the atom. Suppose we could magnify the nucleus of a hydrogen atom up to the size of the sun. Then its solitary electron would be found revolving away somewhere about the orbit of the sun's planet, Pluto, over 3,500 million miles away.

That is space for you, and it is no wonder, consequently, that of a million projectiles fired at a substance, only one would hit a nucleus, all the remainder passing clean through.

By this time it may have occurred to you that, since the electron is regarded as a negative electrical particle, there must be something in the atom with a positive charge to counteract it, otherwise everything we dealt with would be negatively charged, which is not the case. As a matter of fact, the electron is balanced by the proton, a particle carrying an exactly equal and opposite positive charge, but the proton is about 1,840 times as heavy as the electron.

All the protons with their positive

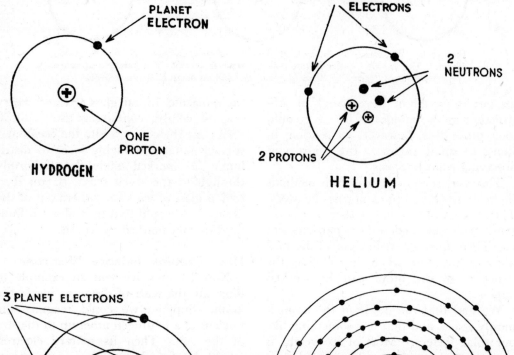

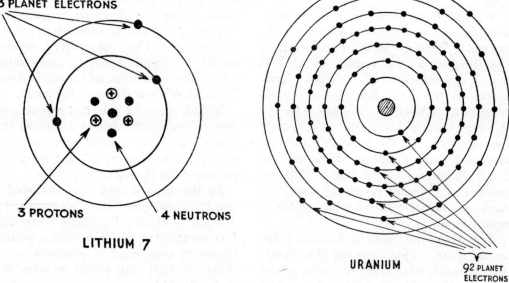

FIGURE 7. *Atomic solar systems, showing how the planetary electrons revolve round the nucleus of protons and neutrons. The diagrams show, (1) the number of electrons in the atom of a particular element and (2) the number of protons and neutrons in the nucleus. In actual fact the planetary electrons would follow elliptical orbits in all directions, and, in the case of heavier elements, their division among many orbits is far more complicated than these diagrams suggest.*

charges are grouped together in the nucleus, the "centre of gravity", so to speak, of the atom, whilst the negative electrons revolve round the nucleus in different orbits at relatively great distances. It should be obvious, therefore, that if there are ten electrons revolving round the nucleus, the nucleus must contain ten protons. That is to say, the nucleus carries a positive charge of ten protons to balance the negative charges of the ten electrons which revolve round it. You will notice that in the nucleus we also have neutrons, so called because they are electrically neutral—that is, they carry neither a positive nor a negative charge. They thus play no part in the electrical structure of the atom, but since they have the same weight as the proton, simply help to "make weight" in the nucleus. For example, the helium atom contains two protons and two neutrons, and its total mass is thus 4, taking the mass of a proton as unity, and neglecting the very small mass of the planetary electrons. An atom of the commonest form of uranium contains 92 protons and 146 neutrons—a total mass of 238. Other forms, like uranium 235, contain fewer neutrons, but because the number of protons remains unchanged at 92, the chemical composition is always precisely the same. Hydrogen, the simplest atom, contains only one proton and no neutrons. Neutrons and protons are not always locked in the nucleus of an atom, however. We can obtain them free, like electrons, and as such are very useful as the atomic missiles we were talking about previously.

What Happens when the Balance is Disturbed

In their normal state, as we have seen, the charges of the electron and proton just balance, so that substances are neutral, but it often happens that, for some reason or other, one or more of the "satellite" electrons, i.e. the electrons revolving round the nucleus, are forced from their orbits and wander about freely. This leaves the atom from which they have come with a positive charge so that it soon attracts to itself again any free electron in its neighbourhood and becomes normal again.

What we have said so far may possibly seem to you a little difficult to understand, but really it all consists of a very simple fact. This fact is that nowadays we consider all matter, all substance, to be ultimately composed of small particles carrying charges of positive and negative electricity. Indeed, some people go so far as to say that matter is actually composed of electricity, or it might be better to express it by saying that in the last resort all matter—a table, a lump of coal, a copper wire—is the result of electrical forces. However, though it may surprise you, with all our knowledge of what an electrical force *does*, we are still quite unable to say what it *is*; our knowledge consists of the effects of such a force so far as we can observe them, but what the force itself may be is as far beyond us today as it was beyond the earliest investigators.

Electrons in Space

In a solid, only the negative charges are free to move, and this being understood it is fairly simple to see how a current flows in a wire. We can imagine electrons being forced from one atom to another along the conductor throughout its length. This means that electrons are transferred from the negative end of the conductor to the positive end. Seeing that there are millions of atoms in a small portion of conductor no bigger than a pin's head, there must be millions of electrons on the move when the current flows, and it is the electrons themselves which constitute the current. In the conductor the electrons move along relatively slowly, say about 1/40 of an inch per second. When they are free, they may move at speeds up to that of light, i.e. 186,000 miles per second.

It may occur to you, however, that text-books on electricity usually show currents as flowing from positive to negative, whereas by our explanation they seem to move from negative to positive. Actually it does not matter which way we look at it, and in fact nowadays, when we are speaking of a current in a wire we generally still look upon it as moving from positive to negative. But, as we shall see later, in the new science of electronics, which deals with currents of electrons in space, it is more convenient to look upon the current as flowing from negative to positive.

And here we return to our currents in space, the sort of currents that Edison observed and recorded in the "Edison Effect". But we are now in a somewhat better position to understand it.

We know, first of all, that any current of electricity can be regarded as consisting of a stream of small, negatively charged particles, that these particles are somehow constituents of all matter, and that under certain circumstances they may be freed from their parent atoms and may exist independently.

We know in the second place that, being negatively charged, they will be attracted to any positively charged body. Now look at Figure 8.

If a current of electricity is crossing the space between the metal plate and the filament, electrons are obviously being freed from somewhere and, attracted by the plate, which has a positive charge, since it is connected to the positive leg of the filament, are passing over to it, thus constituting a "current". Now the only likely source of such electrons is the filament itself. Free electrons are generated whenever the material from which it is composed is made white-hot by the battery current, and we shall see in the next chapter that this is the commonest way of getting swarms of electrons free from a metal.

In a word, we "boil" the electrons out.

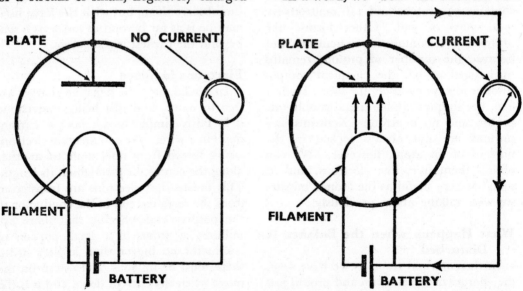

FIGURE 8. *Left, the plate or anode is connected to the negative pole of the battery, and there is no current. Right, it is connected to the battery's positive pole, a current flows between plate and filament, and is shown on the meter.*

Students examining the control panel of the cyclotron machine at the Royal Society Mond Laboratory, Cambridge University. The cyclotron machine is used for the production of neutrons, which it is hoped can be used as a substitute for radium.

Atoms are like tiny solar systems. In the centre is the nucleus (or sun) and around it revolve the electrons (the planets) each in its own orbit.

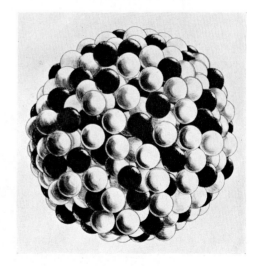

A nucleus is a cluster of closely packed particles of protons and neutrons.

 **E**

Each proton carries a unit positive electrical charge; neutrons have no electrical charge. Electrons carry unit negative electrical charges.

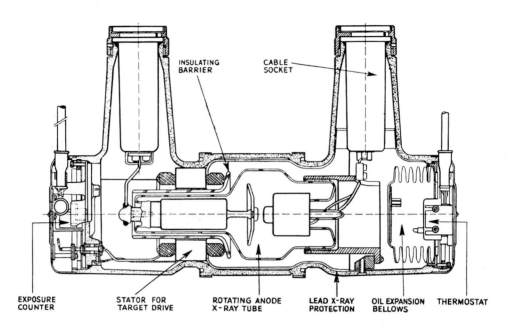

INSULATING BARRIER   CABLE SOCKET

EXPOSURE COUNTER   STATOR FOR TARGET DRIVE   ROTATING ANODE X-RAY TUBE   LEAD X-RAY PROTECTION   OIL EXPANSION BELLOWS   THERMOSTAT

The X-ray tube.   (*line diagram and cutaway photograph*)

An aerial fitted with reflectors.

Short-wave antennae of the Post Office at Rugby.

Short-wave rotating array of Leafield radio station.

Views of the Post Office transmitting station at Rugby built for telegraphy and telephonic communications. (Top left) *Transatlantic and short-wave transmitters.* (Top right) *Valve cabinet with folding iron gate drawn back.* (Below) *Main power house.*

CHAPTER II

THE NEW TOOLS FOR SCIENCE

ONCE MEN had discovered the electron, they began to put it to work, and in doing this they developed three most delicate yet supremely important pieces of apparatus in which flights of electrons were made to perform useful tasks. These three pieces of apparatus are the valve, the photocell and the cathode ray tube, and although they are by no means the only instruments which work by electrons, they are so important, and their uses so varied, that we are going to devote a whole chapter to their explanation. For, if you want to understand wireless you must understand the valve, if you want to understand television you must understand the photocell, and if you want to understand radiolocation you must understand the cathode ray tube.

Indeed, to get a fairly accurate knowledge of how any of these and other electronic devices work is simple when once you have mastered the action of the three pieces of apparatus named. Hence we shall take them in their natural order.

First in order comes the valve, not merely because it was the first to be invented, but because it established the basic principle from which the other two pieces of apparatus have been evolved. The radio or wireless valve, as already explained, provides us with a means of starting currents in space, these currents being caused by the movement of electrons when those electrons are set free from the atoms of which they form a part. So all radio practice begins with getting electrons in the free state.

The most straightforward manner of obtaining electrons free from their parent atoms, as we have seen, is to heat a substance. Heat is a form of motion. When a substance is heated the energy of its atoms is increased and the electrons revolve more and more giddily in their orbits until a time comes when one or more gets out of control and shoots out.

Perhaps we can compare this with what is called centrifugal force, the force that tends to make a weight fly outward when it is whirled round and round. Most of us have experimented with a small weight on the end of a piece of string, whirling it round until the string is stretched out taut, and we know that if we whirl it fast enough and the string is not very strong, the strain may quite possibly snap the string and allow the weight to fly away.

Exactly the same sort of thing happens when the electrons whirl too fast in the atom. Their speed of rotation eventually becomes so great that whatever power it is that holds them to their orbits round the nucleus tends to break down, much as in the case of the string and the weight when the string is not strong enough to hold it.

Figure 9 shows what happens to that very tough metal tungsten when it is heated to about 3,300 degrees Fahrenheit. Some of its electrons reach a speed of 600 miles per second, break through the metal's surface, and fly into space. As the temperature of the metal increases the electrons speed up, more fly off the surface

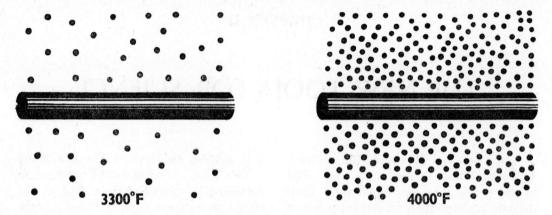

FIGURE 9. *The drawing shows the effect of two different temperatures on a piece of tungsten wire. A temperature of 3,300 degrees F. is needed to drive out even a few electrons. When the temperature is raised only 700 degrees the number of electrons released is more than seventy-five times as great.*

of the metal and, having a still greater speed, reach greater distances from it. At about 4,000 degrees, as the right-hand picture shows, about 75 times as many electrons are released as at the lower temperature on the left.

Freeing Electrons

Under ordinary circumstances they soon fall back into their own or some other atom because, as we have seen, if we rob an atom of an electron we leave that atom with a positive charge, so that any stray electron that comes within range is attracted to it. Nevertheless, there are ways, as we shall see, of removing the freed electrons right out of range of the attractive force so exerted.

One method of heating a wire is to pass an electric current through it, and early wireless valves ("bright emitters") had filaments which were actually run white hot. Subsequently, ways were found of constructing the filament so that it produced a copious swarm of electrons when heated only to a dull red. These filaments were thus called "dull emitters". The dull emitter was an improvement on the first type owing to the fact that it had

a longer life, its wire filament not being subject to so much heat and consequently not suffering so great a strain. But both these valves had the disadvantage of being directly heated. That is to say, the heating current actually passed through the metal wire that acted as the filament and gave off electrons.

Nowadays, however, the usual procedure is to heat the actual cathode, the source of the electrons, indirectly by placing it close to a "heater". The latter is raised in temperature sufficiently to radiate heat to the cathode, which, when it is hot enough, emits electrons. There is a reason for this which you should understand. It makes the actual cathode *independent* of the heating current, and so of fluctuations in that current. Such fluctuations would affect the number of electrons released and so impair the working of the valve. Batteries give a reasonably smooth current, but where current is taken from the mains, fluctuations may be frequent. Hence all "mains" valves are indirectly heated. Figure 10 shows how we indicate a directly heated and an indirectly heated cathode respectively.

The forerunner of the valve was, as we

have seen, Edison's electric bulb with the addition of a plate of metal close to the filament and connected to the positive leg of the latter. Edison made no use of the idea, but it was later studied by the British scientist, Ambrose Fleming, who made the first real valve and so laid the foundation of the new science of electronics.

The Fleming valve was a *diode*—that is, it had *two* elements or main features. These were (1) a filament or cathode, source of electrons, and (2) a plate or anode capable of being raised to a potential of fifty volts or so by connection to the positive pole of a suitable battery. The filament, on being heated by the L.T. battery in Figure 11, emits a swarm of electrons, and if the attractive force of the plate is sufficient, i.e. if its positive potential is high enough, these electrons will be attracted across the space to the plate, forming a current which flows in the plate-filament circuit as shown by the arrow.

The first important use of the diode was as a "rectifier". Suppose in Figure 12

the place of the H.T. battery is taken by a source of *alternating* current, i.e. a current which rapidly changes its direction many times a second, flowing first in a positive direction and then in a negative one, and so on. Now while the A.C. current is flowing in a positive direction the plate will be charged positively and electrons will be attracted across from the glowing filament, and a current will flow round in the direction of the arrows. But when the current changes its direction the plate becomes negatively charged, and since like charges repel, the negatively charged electrons will be prevented from reaching the anode, and *no* current will flow.

Consequently, current will only flow between cathode and anode when the latter is positively charged, so that we have in the filament-plate circuit a current which, though intermittent, i.e. with regular gaps when no current flows, is all in one direction. An alternating current has been changed into a direct one, or, as the scientist would say, it has been rectified.

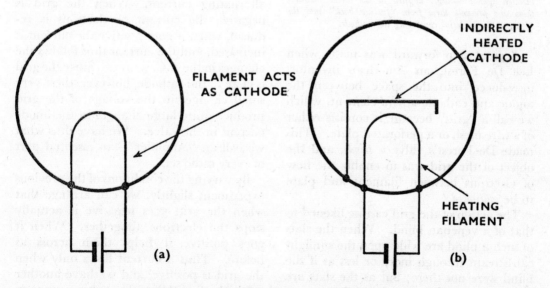

FILAMENT ACTS AS CATHODE

(a)

INDIRECTLY HEATED CATHODE

HEATING FILAMENT

(b)

FIGURE 10. *In the direct method (a) the filament itself acts as the cathode as well as carrying the heating current. In the indirect method (b) the cathode is a separate plate placed near the heating filament.*

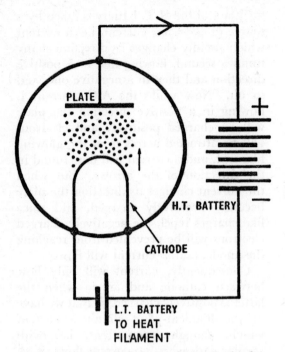

FIGURE 11. *If a high tension battery is placed in the anode-cathode circuit there will be an increase in the number of electrons crossing the gap between anode and cathode, regardless of the temperature of the latter. Heat applied to the cathode releases the electrons from their parent atoms and starts them on their journey through space; voltage, applied to the anode, attracts them and prevents them from "falling back" into the atoms of the material composing the cathode.*

A great step forward was made when Lee De Forest, an American inventor, introduced into the space between the anode and cathode a *third* element, which we call a "grid" because it consists either of a wire mesh or a perforated plate. This made De Forest's valve a *triode*, and the object of the grid was to enable the flow of electrons between filament and plate to be *controlled*.

The action of the grid can be likened to that of a venetian blind. When the slats of such a blind are wide open the sunlight can stream through more or less as if the blind were not there; but as the slats are gradually closed, less and less light penetrates until it is blocked out altogether.

In the same way the grid permits electrons to pass from filament to plate just as if it were entirely absent, but only under certain conditions. Under other conditions it can allow fewer and fewer electrons to pass, and ultimately none at all.

This is not done by altering the grid itself, however, like we adjust the slats of the blind. It is done simply by altering the electric charge on the grid. Figure 13 shows how this is done. A battery of about four volts, called the grid bias battery, is connected with its negative end to the grid and its other end to the cathode. The negative charge on the grid repels the electrons, and fewer get through than previously. By putting in additional batteries, we can make the grid even more negative, thus choking off the electron stream even further, and by putting in enough batteries we can even stop the flow of electrons entirely. We are, in fact, using the valve as a kind of a switch. Now consider what happens, if, as in Figure 14, we connect the grid to a small source of alternating current. When the grid is negative the current of electrons is reduced, when it goes positive the current is increased, and the current thus follows the changes in the A.C. source. Since the grid is close to the cathode, however, these very small changes in the voltage of the grid produce quite large changes in the anode current in the valve. We have thus what we call an "amplifier"—an essential part of every radio set.

By varying the conditions of the previous experiment slightly, we can arrange that when the grid goes negative it actually stops the electrons altogether. When it goes positive it helps them across as before. Thus a current flows only when the grid is positive, and we have another method of making the valve act as a rectifier of A.C. This principle can be

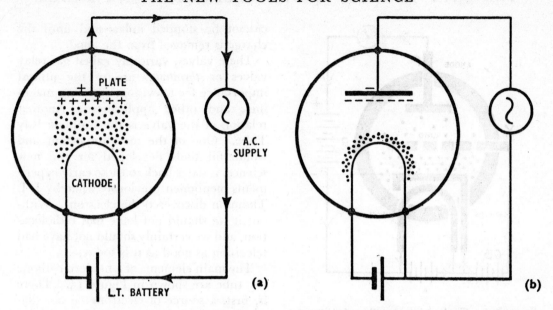

FIGURE 12. *Use of valve as rectifier to turn alternating current into direct current. This was the first important use of the diode, a valve with only two elements, anode and cathode. The place of the usual high tension battery is taken here by a source of alternating current, a current that is continually changing direction. First it flows in a positive direction, then in a negative direction. The fact that it has to flow through the anode-cathode circuit, however, rectifies it into a current flowing in one direction only. This is important because it so happens that it is easier to generate an alternating current than a direct current. The diode valve therefore made things a lot easier for engineers who had to produce a direct current for power purposes.*

used for the detection of wireless waves by your radio set.

Why some Valves are filled with Gas.

Most valves used in radio are vacuum valves, i.e. much care is taken to extract as much air as possible from them so that nothing shall oppose the path of the electrons across the space between filament and plate. In certain valves which are of importance in television, radio-location, and so on, however, a small amount of gas is intentionally inserted into the bulb.

A gas consists of tiny molecules in constant motion. If an electron hits one of these molecules it is quite likely to knock off an electron from the molecule itself, with the result that the molecule, robbed of one of its negative charges, immediately becomes positively charged. Gas mole-

cules in this condition are said to be "ionised".

Suppose we have a triode which contains a small amount of one of the chemically unreactive gases, helium, neon or argon. Suppose, too, that we have a fairly large *negative* charge on the grid, but no charge on the anode. Obviously we shall have no current *through* the valve. If, however, we gradually give the anode a positive charge, there will still be no current in the valve, because the electrons emitted from the cathode are held in check by the negative charge on the grid, and not until the anode charge reaches a value sufficient to overcome the grid's repulsive action will a current start to flow.

Now with an ordinary vacuum valve, when we reach this point, any increase in anode voltage will result in more current flowing, whilst if we decrease the anode

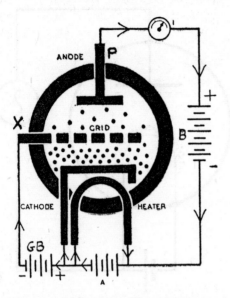

FIGURE 13. *Simple triode, or three-element valve. The new element is the grid. When the grid is negative it does not allow so many electrons to pass across to the anode. When it is neutral it has no effect at all. When positive, it assists electrons to pass across to the anode.*

voltage *below* the critical point again the current will stop.

If there is any gas in the valve, however, things are very different. The electrons moving in the space between the cathode and anode collide with some molecules of the gas and ionise them. This leaves heavy, positively charged gas ions, which are attracted back to the negatively charged grid. Here their action is to nullify its effect, i.e. they collect on it and reduce its negative charge, so that still more electrons can get through the grid into the space beyond. These, in their turn, produce more ions, with the result that in a very short space of time a very large current is flowing. Moreover, this current continues to flow as long as there is *any* charge at all on the anode, and we can reduce the voltage on it almost to zero without stopping the current. Once the current has started to flow, therefore, it builds up quickly to a large value and

cannot be stopped unless and until the charge is removed from the anode.

These valves, variously called gas-relay valves or *thyratrons*, are of the utmost importance for television, counting machines, and other applications. Another relation of the valve is the Cathode Ray Tube. One of the most important and wonderful tools developed for the new science, it dates back to those early experiments mentioned previously whereby J. J. Thomson discovered the electron. Without it we should not have had radiolocation, and we certainly should not have had television as good as it is today.

The main elements of a modern cathode ray tube are shown in Figure 15. There is, first, a source of electrons—a hot fila-

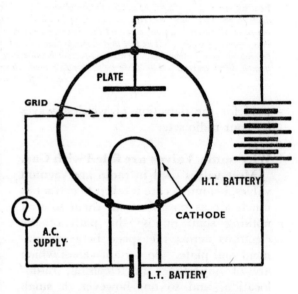

FIGURE 14. *Effect of grid placed between cathode and anode. The grid acts as a "throttle" to control the flow of electrons, and does so according to the strength of the voltage applied to it. When the voltage on the grid is varied, the number of electrons passing through it is varied also, and this gives a more definite control over the flow of electrons than could be obtained merely by varying the voltage on the anode. The introduction of the grid principle was a step forward in the more exact use of the electron, and valves with several grids are now in everyday use. The grid principle is also applied to the cathode ray tube.*

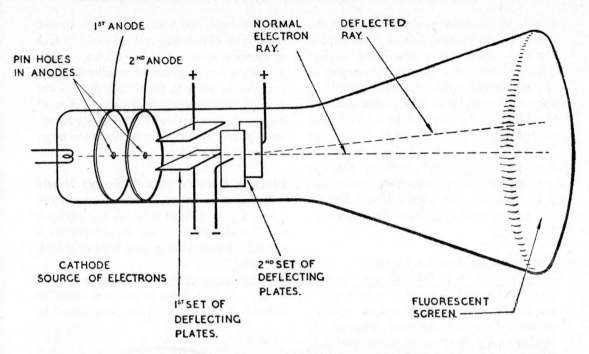

PIN HOLES
IN ANODES.

1ST ANODE

2ND ANODE

NORMAL
ELECTRON
RAY.

DEFLECTED
RAY.

CATHODE
SOURCE OF ELECTRONS

1ST SET OF
DEFLECTING
PLATES.

2ND SET OF
DEFLECTING
PLATES.

FLUORESCENT
SCREEN.

FIGURE 15. *Main elements of the cathode ray tube, consisting of anodes and cathode, the latter being usually of the indirectly heated type, with deflecting plates to control the direction of the stream of electrons. In the valve the electrons flow simply from cathode to anode; in the cathode ray tube they flow from the cathode through the anodes, after which they can be directed to any spot desired on the fluorescent screen.*

ment, or more generally, an indirectly heated cathode. Then there are two anodes, capable of being highly charged, to a thousand volts perhaps, so as to attract the electrons strongly. Each anode, however, has a tiny hole drilled in its centre, so that a very thin pencil of electrons travelling at high speed will go clean through, to fall eventually on the wide end of the tube, which is coated with a material which fluoresces under the impact of the electron ray. Where the ray falls, therefore, will be indicated by a bright spot. We use two anodes in preference to one in order to focus the beam of electrons even better.

The next development is to insert two pairs of plates, one pair arranged horizontally, the other pair arranged vertically. The idea of these plates is as follows:

If one plate of a pair is connected to a battery's positive pole and the other plate to its negative pole, the plates form a *condenser*. Lines of force will stretch between the plates, and any electron traversing this "field" will have its direction changed, the extent of the change depending on the strength of the field.

Hence it is possible, by varying the charge on the vertical pair of plates, to move the spot to and fro *sideways* on the fluorescent screen; but it is also possible, by varying the charge on the horizontal pair, to move it to and fro *up and down*. This means that by arranging suitable charges on the plates we can place the spot anywhere we like on the screen.

A somewhat similar application is the basis of what is called the "oscillograph". Suppose we have an alternating current and we would like to *see* how it rises and falls. All we have to do is to adjust the charge on the vertical pair of plates so that the spot moves slowly across the screen; then we attach our alternating current to the horizontal pair. As the current on these varies, so their field varies, and the deflection of the electron beam will vary accordingly—up and down as the current grows and dies away. I don't think it is hard to see that the result of the *two* motions, both happening at the same time, is to make the spot trace a bright line on the screen something like that shown in Figure 16.

Electrons set free by Light

The photocell, or "electric eye" as it is sometimes called, is another very important tool used in the new science of electronics. It is an essential part of all apparatus for producing talking pictures, television, transmission of photographs by wire and wireless; besides which it is employed in innumerable devices for saving labour.

Photocells, unlike valves which use *heat* to chase electrons out of metals, use *light*. Light is a form of energy, just like heat, and certain substances when exposed to a beam of light liberate electrons very strongly. But after the electrons have actually been liberated they are subject to the same influences as they are in the valve and can be made to act in the same way.

The metals which best show the property of liberating electrons under the influence of light are sodium, potassium, rubidium and caesium, the cathode (electron-liberating surface, taking the place of the filament in the valve) in the photocell being made of a thin sheet of metal coated with a layer of the emitting substance. Even with the metals named, however, the choice will depend on the nature of the light to which it is required to respond.

Sodium, for example, is more sensitive to blue light, caesium to green. In the latest type of caesium cell, in which a film of caesium only a few molecules thick is deposited on a plate of oxidised silver, response is good to nearly all the colours —in particular to red and violet. A most important fact with any type of cell, however, is that the brighter the light the more electrons are emitted.

Electric Eyes to suit Different Needs

Just as in the valve, the electrons emitted when a ray of light falls on the cathode will be attracted by an anode placed a suitable distance away and kept at a high potential.

Photocells may be either of the gas-filled or the vacuum type, in the same way as valves. Traces of gas have been found to

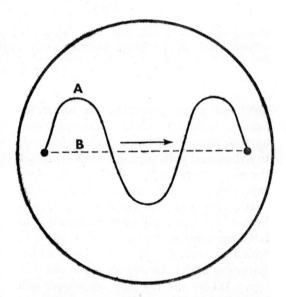

FIGURE 16. *The thick, wavy line (A) shows the sort of graph traced by the stream of electrons when the horizontal deflecting plates are connected to a source of alternating current. The vertical plates are supplied with current of such a nature that the stream moves to and fro in a horizontal direction, as shown by the dotted line.*

By using both movements, from side to side and up and down, it is possible to make the oscilloscope provide a clear picture of how an alternating current varies from one fraction of a second to another.

increase the sensitivity of the cell, since additional electrons are liberated through the collision of liberated electrons with gas molecules (just as in the "thyratron"). However, the gas-filled cell has the disadvantage that it does not respond to light of very high frequencies such as are used in sound-film recording. For this reason the vacuum cell is usually used in practice.

The applications of photocells are so numerous and important that we will deal with them separately and at greater length later (Chapter V).

The X-ray tube

Another kind of electron tube or valve is the X-ray tube. This depends for its effect on the fact that if electrons from a hot filament are attracted to a positively charged plate by a *very* high voltage—up to a million volts—they will have acquired tremendous velocities by the time they strike it. When millions of electrons travelling at high speed strike the anode like this, they cause the metal atoms in it to vibrate. And this vibration causes them to give off radiations almost as powerful as those from radium, and strong enough to penetrate many inches of steel. For a long time, of course, X-rays have enabled doctors to "see" through the human body, but it required the development of much more powerful rays before they could be used for industrial purposes. Nowadays, however, X-rays tell engineers many things about the composition of their castings and forgings, such as the presence of air bubbles inside, and so on, which might later give rise to breakage and dangerous accidents.

CHAPTER III

MAN CONQUERS DISTANCE

LONG BEFORE there was any means of producing them, men knew that wireless waves should exist, they knew the speed at which they should travel, they knew the properties they should possess. This was due to the genius of one man, a Scotsman, James Clerk Maxwell, Professor of Mathematics at Cambridge, who died in 1879.

Twenty-three years later somebody did find a way to produce these waves. He was Heinrich Hertz, a German scientist who, in his laboratory, not only made the waves, but proved that they possessed just the properties which Maxwell had predicted. True, Hertz could only transmit these waves across his room, but they were real wireless waves all the same, and the fact that we can now send wireless messages right round the world if we wish is due to the fact that lately we have had a very powerful friend to assist us—none other than our hero, the mysterious, elusive *electron*.

To attempt to explain abstruse mathematics in simple language is a very bold thing to do, but we shall get to the heart of the matter if I tell you that Maxwell's equations, which deduced for him the existence of wireless waves, were concerned more or less with what happens *when a line of force moves*. Let us examine this statement.

First, what do we mean by a line of force? Suppose you place a bar magnet down flat on the table, cover it with a sheet of thin cardboard, and sprinkle iron filings

thinly over the latter. Then suppose a sharp tap is given to the cardboard. What happens? The result is shown in Figure 17 (*a*), where the filings are shown to have arranged themselves on the card in a special way—in *lines*.

Now although there is no physical connection between the bar magnet and each of the tiny pieces of iron, it is obvious that the former has some influence over them in that it can alter their positions from a distance. And because of the fact that this influence appears to act along lines springing out from the magnet, we have come to explain the phenomenon as being due to "lines of force".

The example we have given referred to lines of force due to a magnet. The existence of electrical lines of force can be shown by the experiment shown in Figure 17 (*b*), where a wire carrying a current passes vertically through a horizontal card on which iron filings have been sprinkled. Here the filings take up positions in circles with the wire as the centre.

Now a curious point is that we could perform these experiments in a vacuum and still get the same results, which proves that the lines of force have nothing to do with the only *known* connection between the magnet and the wire and the outside. The same thing applies to wireless waves. They go through a vacuum or a brick wall equally well. This led scientists to imagine an all-pervading substance which they called the "ether", and lines of force are imagined as stresses and strains in the ether, and wireless waves as something similar.

Why we talk of "Ether" in Space

We say this has led men to *imagine* a substance they call "ether" because there is no proof that any such substance exists. Of course, this ether, except for its name, has no connection with the anaesthetic used by doctors. We postulate the existence of ether in space because it is so difficult to believe in a vibration unless there is something to vibrate, and if we regard space as being "empty" there is nothing at all to give us a vibration. The only thing we could think in that case would be that these tiny electrons, or particles of negative electricity, form a "something" themselves as they travel in space and so provide of their own accord the necessary material which can be set in vibration. At one time the suggestion of an all-pervading ether was generally accepted, but scientists today are not so certain of its existence.

Whether there is such a thing or not matters little, however. What does matter is that lines of stress do exist under the conditions we have described. Now when a line of stress *moves*, some work must have been done, some energy used up. But we know that energy is never destroyed, but only altered in form. Usually it reappears as heat or light.

And here comes the stepping-stone. Both heat and light are *waves*. Waves of what we do not know, so we call them waves in the ether. These waves are distinguishable by their length or their frequency.

Both these terms, length and frequency, occur so often in any discussion of electronics that it will be as well if we get a thorough understanding of them.

If you think of the waves of the sea, their length will be the distance from crest to crest, of the distance from the top of one wave to the top of the wave following it. On the sea, of course, this distance is not always exactly the same, because sea waves are not really regular, being made up of very many different types of waves all mixed up.

But the waves also have a "period", which means the time taken for each wave to sink and rise again. That is to say, if you were standing on a jetty watching a rough sea, you would notice that the water alternately rose to its highest point beside you and then sank again to its lowest point,

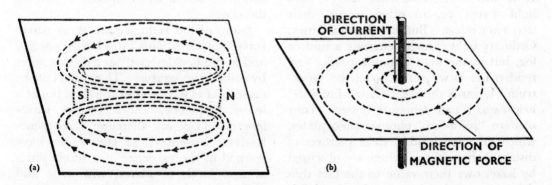

FIGURE 17. *Lines of force surrounding both a bar magnet (a) and a wire carrying an electric current (b). In each case the lines are indicated by iron filings sprinkled on a thin card. When the card is tapped gently, the filings arrange themselves in the manner shown.*

31

the time taken for it to sink from its crest and rise again being its period. The number of such periods occurring in one second is in turn known as the "frequency" of the wave. Frequency and wave-length are interdependent; the length of a wave depends on its frequency, or its frequency depends on its length.

All Radio Waves travel at the same Speed

Suppose you have to walk a distance of fifty yards, and you take steps exactly a yard in length. Then you will take exactly fifty steps to cover the distance. Or if you take steps only a foot long, then the number taken will be one hundred and fifty. But suppose also that no matter what the size of the steps taken you still travel at the same speed; then it is obvious that the shorter your steps the more rapidly you must move your feet.

So if radio waves always travel at 186,000 miles a second, and we have a wave a mile in length, we know that its frequency per second will be 186,000; conversely, if its frequency happens to be only 62,000, we know that its length in miles will be 186,000 divided by 62,000 = 3 miles.

To come back to our point, however. Heat waves are somewhat longer than light waves—or, in other words, their frequency is less. But they *penetrate* better. Ordinary light cannot penetrate a mist or fog, but as the light becomes redder and redder, i.e. as we climb down the "spectrum" towards the red (though invisible) heat rays, it can penetrate better. Your modern "infra-red" photographic plates, which take remarkably clear pictures of distant scenes although these are obscured by haze, owe their value to the fact that they are coated with an emulsion which is sensitive to the penetrating infra-red or heat rays.

The point to consider is that this greater power of penetration appears to be due to the greater length of the wave.

Maxwell's argument, therefore, was roughly this. If we could produce rays (or waves) whose wave-length was longer still than that of the heat rays, these waves should be still more penetrating and should exert their effect over still longer distances. According to his calculations, the waves would have to be about 300 metres long to do this best. But as we have seen, no means was known in Maxwell's time for producing such waves, although Maxwell's argument predicted that they would be produced when lines of force were moved in such a way as to give out, not heat or light waves, but another kind of wave which is not perceivable at all by our senses. These waves he called *electro-magnetic* waves, because they were associated with changes in the electrical and magnetic "fields" at any chosen place, and the waves which Hertz succeeded in producing were true electro-magnetic waves. In essentials, his apparatus consisted, as does the most complicated transmitter today, as a means for rapidly altering the electrical stress or strain in a "circuit", whereby the energy used up appears in the form of electro-magnetic waves which spread out in all directions.

Being of the right length, these waves travel outwards with little loss of energy, and so can be "detected" at a distant point by suitable apparatus. They travel at the same *speed* as light and heat waves, but at a lower frequency, i.e. a greater wave-length. They are therefore more penetrative. Nowadays, of course, we have learned of the existence of a whole series of new kinds of waves, with new and different properties, and Figure 19 (page 34) consists of a chart in which "Hertzian" or radio waves are shown

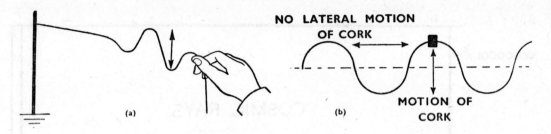

FIGURE 18. *Peculiarity of wave-form illustrated (a) by a rope and (b) by a cork on the surface of the sea. Although in each case the shape of the wave advances, the actual particles of matter of which it is composed do not do so. When a rope is given a sharp up-and-down movement, wave-forms travel along it although no part of the rope is moving forward. Similarly, when a cork is thrown into a rough sea, it tends to remain in the same spot unless driven by wind or tide.*

against a background of all the others.

Wave-motion as an Oscillation

We have already explained wave-motion in part by referring to the waves of the sea, but we now have to consider it as an "oscillation".

A body is said to "oscillate" when it moves uniformly to and fro about some fixed position. A wave-motion is an oscillation, as can be shown from the illustration of a cork floating on the surface of a sheet of water which has been disturbed by dropping something into it. The cork does not move forward with the progress of the wave itself, but moves up and down in a regular motion, being one instant in a "trough" and the next instant on a "crest". This is because the water itself does not move forward; it is only the wave "form" that advances, as shown in Figure 18 (*b*).

To give another example, a pendulum's motion is an oscillation. The bob of the pendulum describes an equal arc on each side of its lowest point, and if friction and air resistance were absent, would continue to do this perfectly uniformly, so many complete swings every minute.

Finally, consider a rope fixed as in Figure 18 (*a*). If we give a long, slow up-and-down movement of the hand, the *whole rope* will follow the movement, except, of course, at the fixed end. But suppose we give a short, sharp movement of the hand. This will be insufficient to move the rope as a whole, but it will impart an up-and-down motion to that portion of the rope nearest the hand, and this movement will be transmitted to the next portion of the rope, and so on, the "kink" in the rope travelling rapidly down the rope itself towards the fixed end. We are, in fact transmitting energy down along the rope.

How an Ether Wave is produced

Now a peculiar thing about this experiment is that when the hand is moved slowly, there is very little motion at the fixed end, but when the movement of the hand is rapid the "kink" or ripple travels down the rope with almost undiminished intensity, and there is quite a large amount of movement at the other end.

We are now in a position to understand roughly how an *ether* wave comes about. It has its origin in the electron. This, we have seen, is a component of all matter, and can be thought of as equivalent to a

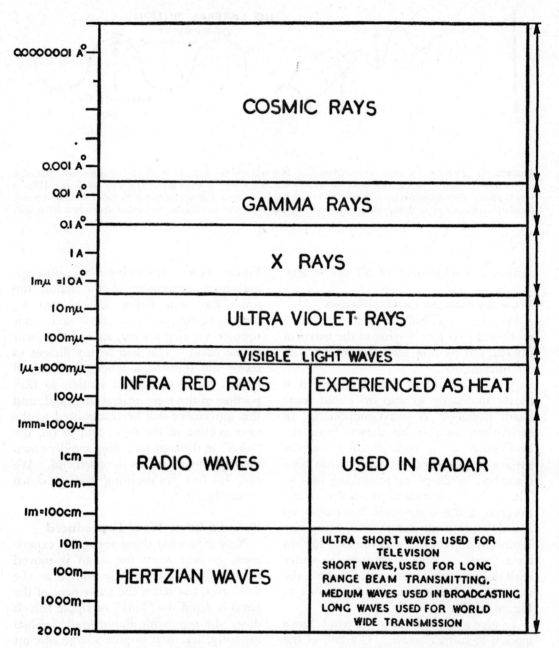

FIGURE 19. *Chart showing wave-lengths of known rays or waves. All these waves are known as electro-magnetic, but light and heat are the only ones that can be perceived by us without instruments. For the perception of Hertzian waves we need a sound or television receiver, and the ultra-violet and X-rays can be seen only by a camera. Gamma rays are penetrating radiations from radioactive substances like radium, while cosmic rays are even more powerful rays of the same sort which reach the earth from outer space.*

Symbols: m metre; cm centimetre; mm millimetre; μ micron; mμ milli-micron; A Ångstrom unit.

tiny, negatively charged particle. Now from any electrically charged body there radiate *lines of force*, and so it must be the same with the electron. Normally, when the electron is moving very slowly, there will be no difficulty in these lines moving with it (the slow up-and-down motion of the rope), but their effect will not be felt at any appreciable distance from the wire or other material in which the electron is moving.

If, however, the electron is given a short, sharp movement, equivalent to an "oscillation", then a sort of "kink" will be started in the lines of force, and this "kink" will move more or less rapidly outwards. Since the lines of force proceeding from the electron are presumed to radiate outwards from it in all directions (Figure 20), the kink or ripple occurring in all simultaneously will take the form of a rapidly expanding shell, which we know as an electro-magnetic wave.

Our job, therefore, is to make an electron—or, better still, a conglomeration of electrons which we call an electric current —oscillate sufficiently rapidly to produce a wave long enough to have the best penetrative powers, i.e. the best "range". This leads us, therefore, to consideration of what we call an oscillating circuit.

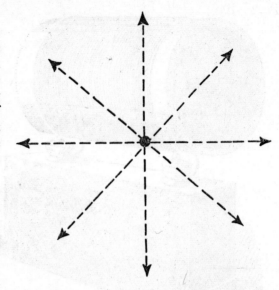

FIGURE 20. *Lines of force radiating from the electron. It is these lines of force, when they are set in motion, that produce a "wave", but they do not do so until the electron is moving rapidly over a wide arc. The electron's normal movement in the atom has to be given a tremendous impetus before lines of force radiating from it become perceptible as a wave. The electron is driven out of its parent atom and is then caused to "oscillate" over a sufficient distance to produce a wave of the required length.*

How an Oscillating Circuit is built up

The simplest oscillating circuit is built up as shown in Figure 21. Let us first see what happens *theoretically* in such a circuit and then we can go on to see how the early experimenters like Hertz and Marconi made use of the arrangement to send wireless messages. Later we can learn how the electron, by means of the valve made communication immeasurably easier, and made radio-telephony possible.

The condenser, C, as its name implies, is a kind of storage tank for electricity. Suppose, then, we charge it up to its full capacity. This means that millions and millions of little negatively charged electrons will be massed on one of the plates, while their absence from the other plate will give this one a positive charge of equal size.

Now suppose that across the terminals of the condenser we connect the coil of wire, labelled I, because its proper name is an inductance. This actually provides a path for the electrons to travel along and we should expect that they would straightway arrange things so that half of them travelled and half remained behind, so equalising the charge on the plates.

Electrons act like a Pendulum

In fact, they do not do this. What

35

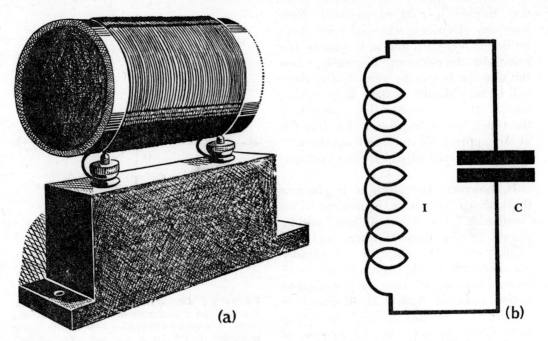

(a)   **(b)**

FIGURE 21. *(a) An oscillating circuit as it actually appears. (b) How we represent an oscillating circuit on a diagram. C is a condenser formed by two metal plates and contained in the metal case on the left, while I is a coil of wire known as an inductance.*

happens, instead, is that immediately the connection is made the electrons tend to rush helter-skelter from one plate to the other and in so doing overstep the half-way mark until the plate which originally carried electrons is completely free of them and they are all congregated on the other. Exactly the same thing happens when we swing a pendulum. The weight at the end of the pendulum, attracted to earth, gathers a "momentum" which carries it past the vertical position until it has reached a height on the other side almost equal to the height from which we released it (Figure 22).

In the case of an electric current flowing through a coil of wire, however, we have an unusual feature to contend with. Any coil of wire carrying an electric current, however small, *will produce a magnetic field*, as can easily be shown by performing the experiment shown in Figure 23. Now the effect of this magnetic field is to *oppose* the current, so that the latter builds up slowly and is not instantaneous. This opposition is maintained until the condenser is empty. When this point is reached there is no voltage left to maintain the current and it begins to die away; but here again Nature tends to oppose any change of existing conditions, and she brings into play forces which tend to *continue* the flow of current. So the current continues for a short space, getting less and less, however, all the time.

The result is that the process of charging the condenser is repeated, but *in the opposite direction*; and here the cycle of events recurs in exactly the same manner. The current commences to flow in the opposite direction, it overshoots the mark, and finally the condenser is once again

The British Broadcasting Corporation is entirely separate from the Post Office and has its own transmitting stations, although Post Office cables are sometimes used for bringing outside broadcasts to the studio. Rugby radio station. (Above) Control table. (Right) The long-wave aerial tuning inductance.

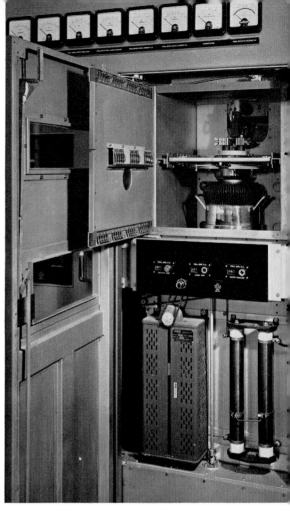

(Top left) *A view of the 32 slots, arranged in eight tiers with four slots in each, in the cylindrical portion of the BBC television and V.H.F. mast near Tacolneston, near Norwich. V.H.F. is radiated from this portion of the mast, whilst the television aerials are mounted above it.*

(Top right) *One half of the transmitter output stage which consists of two valves in parallel positions in an earthed grid circuit, at the BBC V.H.F. transmitting station at Wrotham.*

(Left) *Valve cooling plant at the station at Wrotham: supply unit for the water cooled transmitter test loads. This unit keeps the temperature of the water supplied to the loads at the correct value.*

A general view of the transmitting hall at the BBC V.H.F. station at Wrotham.
Right foreground—the Third Programme main transmitter and standby transmitter.
Right background—the Light Programme main transmitter and standby transmitter.

Power conversion equipment for one of the transmitters at Wrotham.

Main control room at Broadcasting House. All wires lead to the control room whether overland by cable from outside broadcasts or from the studio.

Making a microscope inspection of a groove cut by a disk recording machine.

Demonstration with a mixture of continuous and stroboscopic lighting standing waves on a vibrating string.

A BBC announcer.

Portable transmitting-receiving equipment used for outside broadcasting.

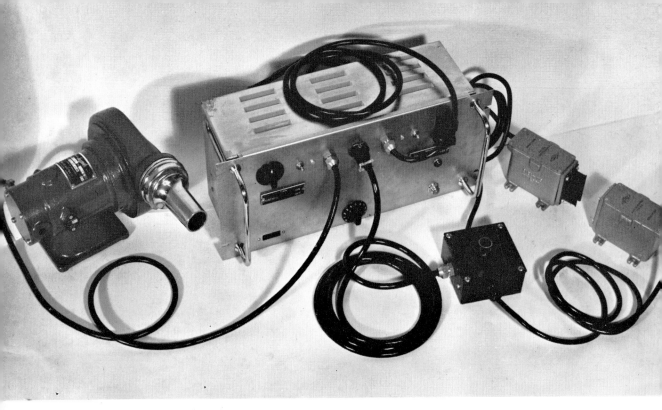

Photoelectric equipment used in manufacturing processes to ensure uniform thickness in the product.

Thickness tester used to examine the state of a propellor.

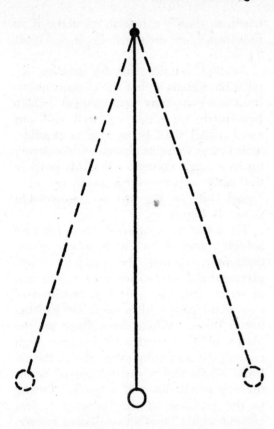

FIGURE 22. *Oscillation of electrons compared with motion of pendulum. When set in motion, the pendulum always "overswings" the position of the vertical line in which it hangs when at rest. The momentum gained on the downward swing carries it over the centre point and up almost to the same height from which it was let go, after which it swings back again and so keeps up the well-known "pendulum motion". The tiny electron does exactly the same thing between the two plates of a condenser. When one plate becomes over-charged with negative electricity, the tendency is for the electrons to flow to the positive plate until the position is reversed.*

charged in exactly the same sense as it was at first.

If you compare the surges of current from one plate of the condenser to the other, through the inductance, with the swinging of a pendulum, you should have no difficulty in understanding the process of producing this electrical "oscillation". And there is another similarity which is

important. The pendulum will not keep on swinging for ever because the air offers resistance to the bob and the arm, and there is always some friction at the hinge. In the same way, the current in the condenser/inductance arrangement will not continue to flow to and fro indefinitely. There is electrical resistance in the circuit which gradually slows down the oscillations, and a condition is finally reached where the condenser is completely uncharged.

A great deal depends, now, on the *sizes* of the condenser and the inductance. If the former is small, it does not hold a large amount of electricity, and so it is rapidly discharged. Correspondingly, if our inductance only consists of a few turns of wire it will not offer much opposition to the growth of the current in it. The latter will therefore rise to its full value very quickly.

By thus adjusting the values of C and I we can arrange for our oscillation to be completed either rapidly or slowly, i.e. we can give the oscillation any desired *frequency*. Now we have seen that what we want for wireless communication is a wave of roughly a certain length. This means a certain frequency—about a million times a second would be suitable —and if what was said previously about the production of ether waves through the movement of electrons was understood it will be realised that there we have all the means for producing such waves. We have a circuit in which electrons rush to and fro between the two plates of the condenser, and we have only to alter the values of the condenser and/or the inductance to give these waves the frequency (and consequently the wave-length) we desire.

But we must also arrange to radiate the energy of our oscillation into space. Figure 24 (*a*) shows how this is done. In

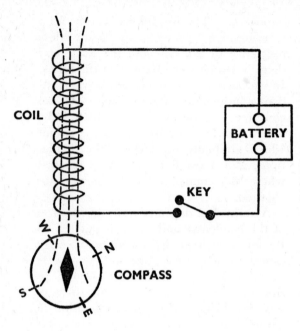

COIL

BATTERY

KEY

COMPASS

FIGURE 23. *Deflection of compass needle by electric current. This is another way of proving that there are lines of force surrounding a wire through which an electric current is flowing. They are known as the magnetic field, and a magnetic field produced by a current always opposes the flow of that current, the resistance being greater when the wire is in the form of a coil. When a current is made to flow through a coil it builds up to its full strength only slowly, and conversely, when it attempts to change direction, the coil again opposes the sudden change. A resistance such as a coil of wire therefore helps the oscillation so that the flow of electrons between the two plates of a condenser is sent back and forth as many times as possible from the original impulse given by the charge on one plate.*

the first place our condenser consists of a pair of plates, one carried in the air, the other buried in the ground. These plates inductance is included in it (Figure 24 (*b*)).

The logical development then was to substitute two or more wires for the upper plate of the condenser and make the earth itself constitute the other plate. Even a single vertical wire, as you know from experience, possesses some capacity to

earth, so that it can form an aerial if an inductance is included in it. (Figure 24 (*b*)).

Another requirement for sending intelligible signals is that the current in our inductance-capacity arrangement (which henceforth we might as well call our *aerial system*) shall be as *large* as possible. This means we must charge our condenser up to a large voltage. For this purpose the early experimenters made use of a "spark-coil" in the sort of arrangement shown in Figure 25.

The job of the spark-coil was to produce a high voltage between the plates of the condenser. Across the condenser was arranged the inductance with a *spark* gap in series with it. This gap consisted of two metal balls with a short air gap between them. When the voltage on the plates of the condenser became high enough the insulating properties of the air broke down and a current passed across the gap in the form of a spark. Owing to the presence of the inductance, this current would be of an oscillating nature. Its frequency depends on the height of the aerial which is coupled to the inductance. If this is large, the frequency of the oscillation is low, because the capacity of the aerial is correspondingly large; the current, however, will be large too, because the condenser part of our aerial system can hold a very big charge.

The great Post Office station at Rugby, with masts 800 feet high, sends out waves up to eleven miles long. These have very great penetrative power, but the power supplied to the aerial has to be several hundred kilowatts. As a matter of fact, the greater the aerial capacity the greater the power needed to transmit a strong enough wave, and this puts a limit on the length of wave-form used.

As we have seen, the purpose of the transmitter is to generate waves, or regions

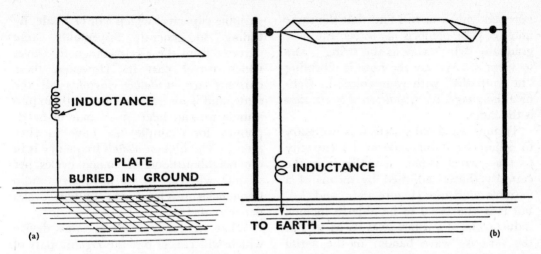

FIGURE 24. *The earth and aerial in effect form a condenser with a greater distance between the "plates", and the vertical wire that joins them includes the inductance (resistance). By altering the size of the plates and the size of the inductance, any desired frequency of oscillation can be obtained.*

of stress and strain, in the "ether". We produced these waves by the movement of electrons in a vertical wire.

If now we erect a vertical wire at some distance from the transmitter, we shall get the contrary effect. The changing stresses and strains will be communicated to the electrons in the wire, tending to make them move, and we know that electrons in motion constitute an electric current.

Electric voltages, and therefore currents, are set up in such a receiving aerial.

Naturally, they are exceedingly small, with strengths in the neighbourhood of a few millionths of a volt, depending on the distance from the transmitter.

This state of affairs can fortunately be overcome by a process called "tuning" the aerial. The principle of "tuning" can be illustrated by many examples. Here is a very simple one. Open your piano at the top and, if you like, take out the front. Put your foot on the loud pedal, and sing a loud, clear note. If you break off this

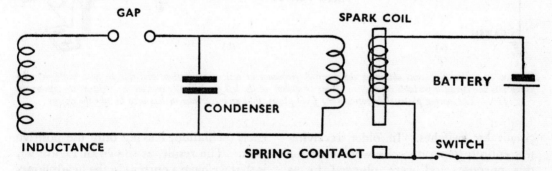

FIGURE 25. *Wiring of early spark coil transmitter. The object of the gap is to offer resistance to the passage of the current so that it builds up to as high a voltage as possible. When it is sufficient to cause a spark to leap the gap the surge of electrons starts an oscillation in space whose frequency depends on the relative sizes of aerial, inductance and condenser.*

note suddenly you will find that the same note on your piano is *responding*, the note gradually dying away as the string ceases to vibrate. We say the note is vibrating "in sympathy" with your voice; in technical language, its *natural period of vibration* is the same.

To tune an aerial system it is necessary to adjust its inductance or its capacity to the correct value. Usually it is the capacity that is adjusted by means of a variable condenser (Figure 26 (*a*) and (*b*)), but it is also usual to be able to include inductances of various sizes so as to suit the various "wave bands" in the aerial

variable capacity) which can be made, by tuning, to generate respectably large currents from the electro-magnetic waves which travel past it. However, these currents are *oscillating* currents all the same, and if we want to convert them into sounds we can hear—in a pair of headphones, for example—we have to alter them. The highest *audible* frequency is in the neighbourhood of 20,000 cycles per second, whereas, as we have seen, radio frequencies reach several million cycles per second.

What we really want is some device which will cancel out the *negative* part of

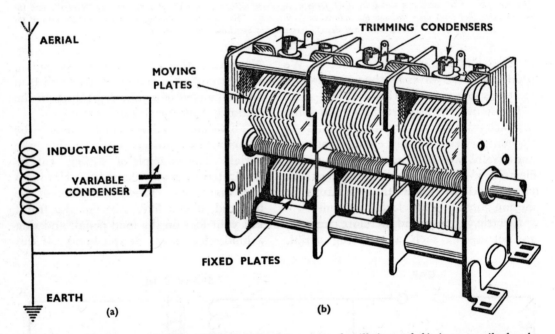

FIGURE 26. *Tuning means obtaining the required frequency or rate of oscillation, and this is most easily done by fitting into the circuit a variable condenser. This is shown on the left symbolically and on the right as it appears in fact. The moving plates slide between the fixed plates, thus giving greater or less area to take the charge.*

circuit by switches. In older receiving sets entirely separate coils were used for this purpose, and were plugged in as required.

We now have at the receiving end an aerial system (including inductance and

each oscillation, leaving only the positive part. The result, as shown in Figure 27, is that we have a current in the headphones which flows always in the same direction, but which varies in that there are gaps in it, and it rises and falls with a regular

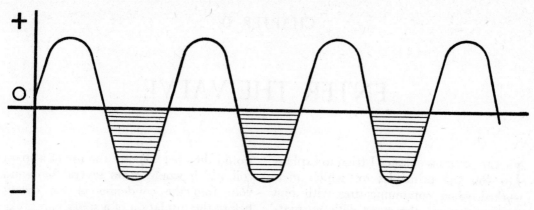

FIGURE 27. *Graph showing that the current in the headphones must flow always in the same direction. It must also, of course, be of a sufficiently low frequency to be audible, but that is not enough. We have to turn the alternating current into direct current for loudspeaker or headphones.*

frequency which produces a musical note in the phones.

With the old spark transmitter it was only possible to send out a train of waves every time a spark occurred, and these waves were rapidly "damped out" by losses in the circuit (Figure 28). When the valve came on the scene, however, it became possible to send out waves which were "continuous", and these continuous waves could be so "modulated" that they corresponded to the varying tones of a piece of music or a song.

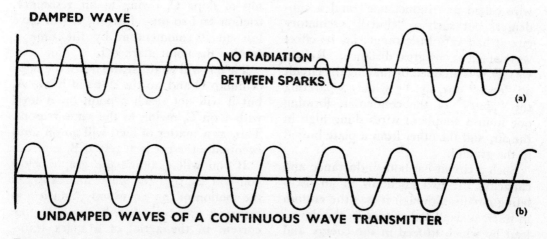

FIGURE 28. *In the spark coil type, (a) an oscillation of the ether was set up only when a spark jumped the gap; there was no radiation between the sparks, and the wave was continually rising and falling in value from start to stop. The continuous wave transmitter sets up a steady wave which continues all the time.*

CHAPTER IV

ENTER THE VALVE

IN THE previous chapter I tried to explain to you the principles on which men worked when communicating with one another through the ether with no material link joining transmitter and receiver.

I explained first how, if an electron were made to oscillate or vibrate rapidly, "kinks" were formed in the lines of force radiating from the electron, and these "kinks" travelled outward along the lines of force, sometimes to immense distances, just as the "wave" travelled along the rope.

We saw, then, how the electron was set into the necessary state of vibration or oscillation in an *oscillating circuit*. This circuit consisted essentially of a coil of wire called an "inductance" and a condenser, but such a "closed" oscillatory circuit had very little range, i.e. its effect was not felt at any great distance. Range, we saw, was attained by making the circuit an "open" one, i.e. by widely separating the "plates" of the condenser, forming one from a couple of wires slung high in the air, and the other from a plate buried in the ground.

Such a circuit has both inductance and capacity, the two essentials in an oscillating circuit, although it was the custom to insert a small inductance in the downlead by which to feed in the energy and for the important purpose of "tuning".

Finally, we saw that the more energy we could cause to swing to and fro in the oscillatory circuit, the more powerful would be the waves radiated through the ether from it, and the more penetrating would they be. Hence the use of a spark coil which would cram several thousand volts into the condenser of the circuit before the insulation of a spark gap broke down, releasing all this pent-up energy into the aerial.

Now the great disadvantage of this arrangement was that the waves sent out were "damped". This can best be explained by an illustration. Suppose we had a switchback arranged as in Figure 29 (*a*). If a car starts off down the slope of hump A it will have attained sufficient momentum by the time it reaches the bottom B to carry it on up the slope of hump C. But it will not quite reach the top of slope C, owing to air resistance, friction and so on. Instead, it will have lost all its momentum by the time it reaches the point marked 1.

Then it will set off again, down the slope of hump C and up the slope of hump A, but it will not reach a point on A level with 1 on C, owing to the same reasons. This, as a matter of fact, will go on until eventually the car is at rest at B.

If you will examine the graph below you will see that the wavy line expresses the motion of the car exactly, and it also expresses exactly what happens to the current in the aerial of a spark transmitter. The shape of the graph, moreover, is exactly the shape of the waves sent out from such a transmitter.

These "damped" trains of waves were not unsuitable for sending messages by Morse. Remember that many of them

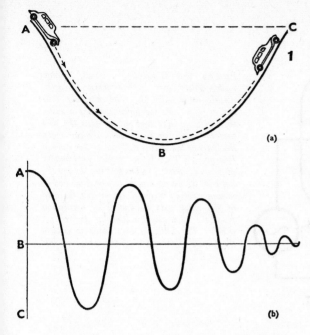

(a)

(b)

FIGURE 29. *Damped waves illustrated (a) by action of car alone on slope and (b) diagrammatically. If the car starts from the point A at the top of the left-hand slope and is allowed to run freely down the hill, it will overshoot the lowest point B and ascend the right-hand slope almost to C, on a level with A. But it will never quite reach the level from which it started. The momentum gathered as it descended from A will always be insufficient to carry it right to the top again, because a certain amount of effort is lost in overcoming friction. The car will then merely run backwards up the A slope to a point not quite so high as it has reached on C, and finally goes on running backwards and forwards on a run that gets shorter and shorter until eventually it comes to rest at B. This is what happens to a damped wave.*

are sent out every second, and if a dot in the Morse code lasts two seconds it can easily be distinguished from a dash, which lasts twice as long. But the problem of transmitting actual speech or music, as in broadcasting, is different. It requires, as we shall see, a *continuous* wave, and until the valve had been perfected continuous waves could not be produced.

Our first job, then, in learning about broadcasting, is to find out how the losses

in our oscillatory circuit—which losses are the cause of "damping"—can be made up so that, to go back to our switchback example, the car swings back and forth from just near the top of slope A to just near the top of slope C with undiminished vigour.

That is where the valve comes in, and we can best explain its action by referring again to the principle of a pendulum.

The pendulum of a clock swings, day in, day out, without slowing down, but it is constantly receiving energy. Every time it swings back it is given a little push by a toothed wheel driven by a heavy weight. The essential thing, however, is that the pendulum itself releases this escapement wheel at the right moment (otherwise the clock would not go) and so controls the working of the clock.

The problem with an oscillatory circuit is just the same. The circuit corresponds to the pendulum. It needs constant energy—taken from a battery. This battery corresponds to the weight in the clock. This energy must be supplied at the right moment, and whereas the clock-maker employs an escapement wheel which is released at the right moment by the pendulum itself, we use a valve—a triode—whose *grid* is operated by the oscillating circuit itself, so that a current impulse is always let through at the right moment.

A simple type of Oscillating Circuit

In practice, therefore, we could hook up a circuit such as that shown in Figure 30. Notice that the coil L in the aerial circuit is also connected to the anode circuit of the valve. When a current alternating at the frequency of radio waves is applied to the *grid* of the valve, it will be obvious from our previous knowledge of what happens in a valve that the anode current will vary also with the same frequency.

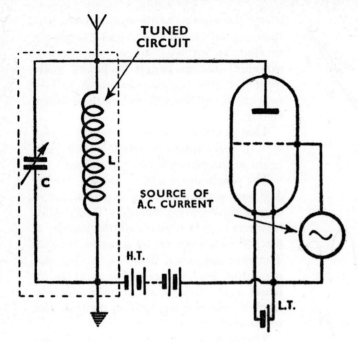

TUNED CIRCUIT

L

C

SOURCE OF A.C. CURRENT

H.T.

L.T.

FIGURE 30. *Oscillating circuit, shown within dotted lines. This consists of earth, aerial, inductance (L) and variable condenser (C). By the balance of these units, their relative size and so on, plus the fact that the condenser is variable, we can make this part of the circuit oscillate at any desired frequency. This is a simple, explanatory diagram of what is meant by "tuned circuit", but Fig. 31 shows a more practical method of wiring such an arrangement so that the grid of the valve gets its period of oscillation from the oscillating section of the circuit itself. The latter is thus made to control the period of vibration of the whole circuit.*

Thus there will be generated in the coil L a current which varies with a frequency equal to that of radio waves—in other words, the aerial circuit is *driven* at the same frequency as the current applied to the grid, and if the aerial is tuned to *resonance* (Chapter III) by the variable condenser C, the current flowing in the aerial circuit will be a maximum, and so will the amount of energy radiated by the aerial system.

This is not a very practical arrangement, however, so we go a step forward by adopting a circuit such as that shown in Figure 31. Here the radio-frequency current applied to the grid may be obtained from the oscillating circuit itself.

In this arrangement there is a second coil, L_2, coupled magnetically to the aerial coil, L_1, and once the current is switched on, the circuit continues to oscillate for as long as we like. What happens is as follows:

As soon as the cathode has heated up,

a current flows across to the anode and goes from there to the oscillatory circuit formed by the aerial and the inductance-capacity arrangement $C-L_1$. So the aerial commences to oscillate at radio frequency.

Meanwhile, the radio-frequency current in L_1 has induced a radio-frequency current in L_2, which imparts to the grid a potential which varies at radio-frequency. This in turn causes a radio-frequency variation in the anode current, hence a radio-frequency voltage across L_1. Thus the aerial oscillations are maintained.

This is called a self-oscillator. It is the usual method of generating a radio-frequency current. The actual source of the energy applied to the aerial is, of course, the high-tension battery in this case, the valve merely acting as a linking mechanism, doling out the energy in a series of pulses which are automatically timed by the aerial circuit itself.

The waves travelling out from the transmitting aerial penetrate the air, and the air is full of electrical "life". It is full of electrons, and ions, which are gas molecules which have temporarily lost one or two of the electrons which travel round the central nucleus in relatively distant orbits. And if a molecule of a gas loses an electron it loses a small negative charge, i.e. it becomes positively charged.

The formation of ions is due to ultraviolet radiation in the sunlight—atoms seem to gather in their lost electrons again at night—so that at night the air is electrically "stiller" than during the day, and this has an important consequence in broadcasting. These electrically charged particles are all thrown into violent oscillation by the ether waves, which are thereby robbed of some of their energy. That is why radio waves are more powerful at greater distances during the night than during the day; reception is also better in the dark days of winter.

From prehistoric times the natives of Africa have telegraphed to one another by means of very deep-toned, rumbling drums—in other words, by means of very long sound waves. And we know by experience the long, slowly-oscillating (low-frequency) waves penetrate better than short ones, and that is the reason for the use in early transmitters of waves up to twelve miles in length! However, we have learned something since then.

Why Short Waves Travel Great Distances

A ten- or twelve-mile wave runs along the surface of the globe, and the electrical lines of force are at right angles to the earth's surface. They run along the ground as they would along a wire. We call such waves "ground waves". The shorter the wave the larger the fraction which escapes from the ground; indeed, it was formerly supposed that below one hundred metres the waves were entirely lost in space.

However, certain American amateurs to whom this useless band of wave-lengths was generously surrendered surprised

FIGURE 31. *Oscillating circuit that controls the radio-frequency current supplied to the grid. Besides the inductance (L_1) in the tuned circuit (shown within dotted lines) there is another coil (L_2) wired to the grid of the valve. The effect of this arrangement is that any oscillation that takes place in the tuned circuit is induced in the rest of the circuit, so that the grid of the valve is controlled by it. Such a circuit is known as a self-oscillator. This is the usual method of generating a radio-frequency current. The valve gives forth a series of pulses which are timed or controlled automatically by the tuned aerial circuit.*

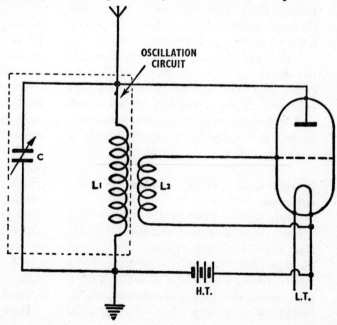

everyone by transmitting with them over immense distances with powers which were only a tiny fraction of those employed on the commercial wave-lengths. We now know the reason.

At a very great height above the earth—sixty or seventy miles—there is a strongly conducting *layer* of electrically charged particles (ions), called from its discoverer the *Heaviside* layer. This dense layer of ions does nothing other than *reflect* back the radio waves, a property that has enabled its height to be determined exactly.

A short, sharp signal is sent vertically upwards, is reflected at the layer, and returns to earth about a thousandth of a second later. Now as we shall see in dealing with radar, small intervals of time like this can now be measured very accurately, and, knowing that 300,000 kilometres a second is the speed of *all* electro-magnetic waves, including light and radio waves, it is a simple matter to calculate the layer's height.

Thus it is that *short waves* travel up to what we call the "ionosphere", are reflected from the Heaviside layer and directed back to earth, which they may hit several thousands of miles distant.

Unfortunately, the Heaviside layer is not *stable*; it is more like a billowing cloud, and may become for a time a bad reflector. Then reception grows weak and indistinct, only recovering when the layer has become calm again. This is known as *fading*.

Interference with Radio Transmission

Then again, there is the question of "interference". Every electrical oscillation, every variation of a current, propagates an electrical disturbance through the ether, although the range at which such a disturbance can be felt is relatively short. Switching on a lamp, working a vacuum-cleaner or an electric motor, illuminating an electric sign—all these things create disturbances in the ether which are picked up by the receiving aerial and translated in the set into "local noise".

We have now come to the point where we understand how it is possible to have a transmitter which sends an alternating electric field out into the ether—a continuous succession of waves—but we are still in the dark as to how this can help us to attain to modern broadcasting.

In the first place, even though we feed thousands of watts of energy into our aerial, this energy is simply dissipated into space, and although its effect *is* observable at a very great distance owing to phenomena which have been described, the energy we should be called upon to detect measures only a tiny fraction of a watt.

Radio Frequencies too High to be Heard

In the second place, if our waves are to be of the most penetrating variety, we have seen that they must have wave-lengths which lie within a certain *range*, say between 150 and 550 metres if we leave out the very long wave-length stations which require enormous powers to drive them. Now we have learned that the speed of these waves (300,000 kilometres or 300,000,000 metres per second) divided by their wave-length (say, 300 metres on the average) gives us their *frequency*, i.e. the number of complete vibrations performed per second. Our average frequency, therefore, is about one million cycles per second, or 1,000 kilocycles. However, the average frequency of the waves to which our ears are sensitive is approximately 20,000 oscillations per second, so that a telephone or a loudspeaker vibrating at radio frequencies would give a note quite beyond range of hearing.

How are these two problems got over?

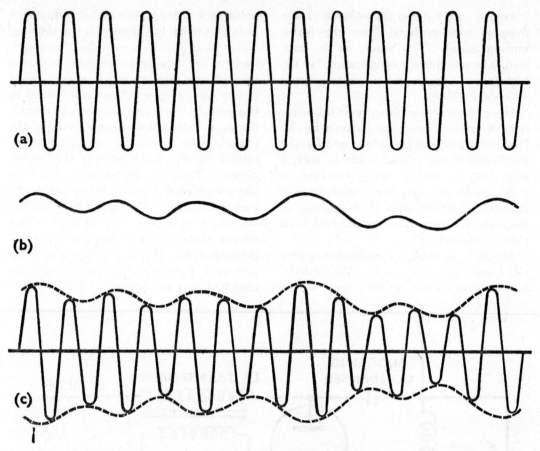

FIGURE 32. *In the top figure (a) is shown a train of undamped waves such as are transmitted by a continuous transmitting aerial system, while the irregular wavy line (b) represents speech or music. This is no good for transmission at the tremendously high oscillation known as radio-frequency, so the speech current is made to influence the otherwise steady train of pulses at radio-frequency already generated by a tuned aerial system, and thus we make the radio-frequency waves transmit the irregular shape of sound (c).*

The first will be dealt with when we come to regard the valve as an *amplifier*, so we will hold over its consideration for the moment. The second we have to go into carefully, for it involves the important principle of "modulation".

Although we have not yet described the *microphone*, we can anticipate matters by explaining that it is the job of this instrument to translate sound into electrical terms. In other words, out from the microphone goes an electric current which *varies in amplitude* according to the varia-

tions in sound which strike it. If this varying current is fed to a telephone receiver, it will, in turn, make the diaphragm of the receiver vibrate in harmony and will thus produce sound waves corresponding to the sound waves which struck the microphone.

However, in wireless we have no physical connection between the transmitting microphone and the telephone earpiece. All we have is a continuous electro-magnetic wave, radiated by the transmitting aerial.

Figure 32 (*a*) shows the *continuous radio-frequency wave* radiated from the transmitting aerial. This wave, as we have seen, has a frequency of vibration far too high to make any sound in our telephones which is audible.

However, it is possible to make this wave *carry the audio-frequency wave* shown in (*b*). In other words, it is possible to *modulate* the amplitude of the carrier wave in such a way that, instead of being constant, it varies as in (*c*), and the variations will correspond exactly with the variations in the audio-frequency current received from the microphone (*b*).

Figure 33 shows in a simplified way how this result can be obtained. We feed the high-tension current to the anode of the

valve, not through the aerial inductance as in Figure 31, but through a transformer. This transformer is of the "step-up" variety, i.e. if a small current is passed through the primary winding and varied in any way, a large voltage will appear in the secondary winding and vary in exactly the same way. Now in our example the variations of current in the primary are caused by the voice striking the microphone. Thus the high-tension reaching the anode of the transmitting valve will vary in exactly the same way as the speech currents in the microphone. This means that the radio-frequency current generated by the valve because it is part of a self-oscillating circuit will be modified, or "modulated", by the sounds

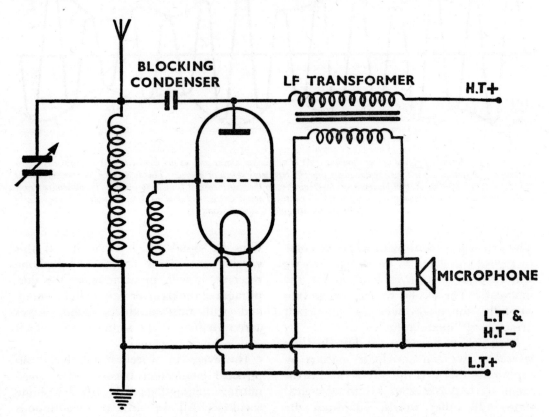

FIGURE 33. *Method of connecting aerial system to microphone so that the radio-frequency current is modulated by the speech current. The current is fed to the anode of the valve through a transformer.*

occurring in front of the microphone.

The radio-frequency or "carrier" wave, then, acts in place of the wire joining two telephone sets. Its *shape* has been changed to correspond to certain sounds which were poured into the microphone. All we need to do in our receiver is to unravel the continuous radio-frequency part from the audio-frequency component, for it is only the latter we want; the former, as we have seen, is of no use to us. Before we consider this task in detail, however, we should look a little more closely into the construction of that interesting instrument, the microphone.

The Microphone and how it works

A common form of microphone is that termed a carbon-granule microphone. The principle on which this works is shown in Figure 34. The disc or diaphragm is held firm by its rim, but free to vibrate otherwise. Contact between the disc and the backplate is made through carbon granules packed neither too tightly nor too loosely in between. When sound waves strike the diaphragm the pressure of the latter on the carbon granules is varied, and the action of the microphone is based on the fact that the electrical resistance between two pieces of carbon is proportional to the pressure they exert on one another. Hence the resistance of the whole circuit shown in Figure 34 varies in accordance with the sound waves; and if the resistance of the circuit so varies, the current flowing in it must vary in exactly the same way.

To convert the rather weak effect in the microphone into a stronger one we connect the instrument to the primary of a step-up transformer, which, by means of the secondary, impresses the same variations on the high-tension supply to the valve. The electro-magnetic microphone, on the other hand, works in a diff-

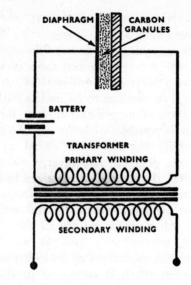

FIGURE 34. *The object of any microphone is to translate sound waves into electrical impulses, which means that the instrument must be such that it causes sound to affect current. The carbon granule microphone is based on the fact that carbon offers a varying resistance to the passage of an electric current according to the pressure exerted upon it. In this microphone, therefore, the diaphragm is so placed that it is free to vibrate under the influence of sound waves, and yet in contact with a packed mass of tiny carbon granules. As the diaphragm vibrates, the pressure it exerts on the granules is varied, and the granules will therefore offer a varying resistance to the electric current which passes through it to the primary winding of the transformer. Thus the current supplied to the aerial system will vary according to the sound reaching the microphone.*

erent way. A very light conductor is suspended in a strong magnetic field, and sound waves striking it cause it to vibrate. When a conductor in a magnetic field *moves*, it has electric currents generated in it, and the strength of these corresponds to the extent of the movement.

What happens at the Receiving End

At the receiving end, which is, for most of us who listen to broadcasting, the end that matters, the first problem is to pick up the signal. This is done usually by means of an aerial in which the wireless waves set up minute currents; whereas the power forced into a transmitting aerial may be anything up to 100 kilowatts or more, the receiving aerial may pick up less than a microwatt (millionth of a watt).

This is so small as to be useless without some form of amplification, but fortunately it is possible, with the aid of valves, to amplify the incoming signal to the required degree. However, although amplified, the signal is unchanged in form —it still consists of a radio-frequency "carrier" which has been "modulated" by the speech currents set up in the transmitting microphone, and as we have learned, the vibrations at radio-frequency are useless when it comes to producing audible sounds from the telephones or loudspeaker.

In some way we have to *disentangle* the audio-frequency vibrations from the radio-frequency vibrations, and this we call "demodulation" or "detection". After demodulation we are left with an audio-frequency or low-frequency signal which, although of the right type to operate a loudspeaker or headphones, is usually still too weak to do this satisfactorily. It is customary, therefore, to follow detection, or demodulation, with a stage of what we naturally call low-frequency amplification.

A simple type of Receiver

A very simple radio receiver, therefore, will consist of some arrangement whereby the receiving aerial can be "tuned" to the frequency of the waves from the broadcasting station it is desired to listen to, just as the transmitting aerial itself is tuned. The signal will then first be amplified, then demodulated, and finally the demodulated signal will again be amplified before being passed to the loudspeaker. It should be noted, however, that it is not absolutely necessary to amplify the radio-frequency signal before demodulating it. Many simple receivers demodulate the signal directly it is received, and rely for volume on, say, two stages of low-frequency amplification.

All three processes—R.F. amplification, detection or demodulation, and L.F.

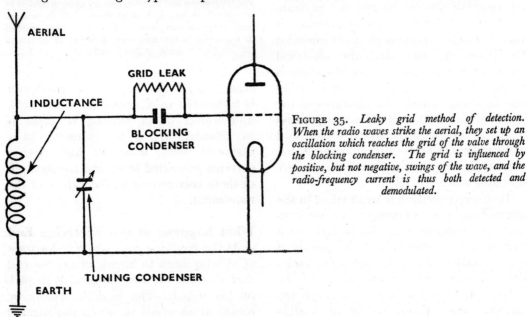

FIGURE 35. *Leaky grid method of detection. When the radio waves strike the aerial, they set up an oscillation which reaches the grid of the valve through the blocking condenser. The grid is influenced by positive, but not negative, swings of the wave, and the radio-frequency current is thus both detected and demodulated.*

amplification—depend on particular properties of the *valve*.   In the first and the last
it is the valve as *amplifier* with which we
are concerned; in the second it is with the
valve as *detector* that we deal.   From what
was said about valves in Chapter II you
should already have a good idea of the
fundamental principles involved.

"Leaky Grid" Method of Detection

We saw in Chapter II a method whereby a valve can be made to act as a demodulator or detector, but the one you
probably know best is the "leaky grid"
method.   For most purposes it is the most
convenient and practical.

Suppose we set up a circuit on the lines
of the wiring diagram shown in Figure 35.

In this arrangement the charge on the
grid depends on the incoming signal, which
reaches it via the condenser, which blocks
direct current but allows radio-frequency
current to pass.   Positive swings of the
carrier voltage cause the grid and condenser to acquire a charge of negative
electrons from the filament, which is not
affected by the negative swings of the
carrier.   Soon the grid becomes charged
up to nearly the same voltage as that of
the carrier input, and thereafter the carrier
merely compensates for the steady leakage
of charge from the grid through the grid
leak.

The grid acquires a steady negative
bias if the carrier is *not* modulated.
Modulation of the carrier merely alters the
charge on the grid according to the
variation it produces in the carrier, and
the grid charge that is thereby produced
is merely a copy of the modulation voltage.

This is what we want, since variation in
the grid charge produces corresponding
variations in the valve anode current.
Any load in the anode circuit will therefore have generated across it a voltage
which follows the grid voltage, but is

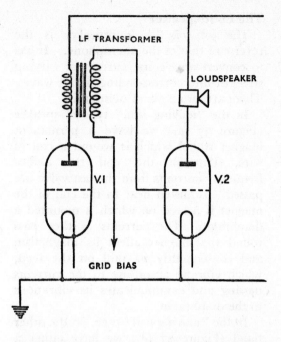

FIGURE 36.   *The valve as amplifier.   In this circuit
the detector valve (V1) and an amplifying valve (V2) are
wired to the loudspeaker.   The anode current from V1
is passed to V2 by means of a step-up transformer, so
that it is increased in voltage even before reaching the
amplifying valve.   The higher voltage is applied to the
grid of the amplifying valve V2, where it causes even
greater changes in the anode current flowing through the
loudspeaker.   This is an example of what we call low
or audio-frequency amplification.*

higher owing to the amplification of the
valve.

Hence the grid detector not only de-
modulates, but amplifies as well.   We
saw previously that this amplifying action
depended on the fact that although the
fluctuations in the grid voltage are only
minute, the current they control in the
anode circuit is large.   For audio-frequency amplification the anode current
through the detector valve can be applied
to the primary of a step-up transformer
(Figure 36) whereby it is still further
amplified in conjunction with the last
valve of the circuit.

The Loudspeaker

The job of the loudspeaker is the reverse of that of the microphone. It has to convert an electric current of varying strength into corresponding sound waves. There are two ways of doing this.

In the "moving iron" type of speaker (Figure 37 (*a*)) we have a permanent magnet round which is wound a coil of wire. Through this coil the audio-frequency currents from the last valve are passed. Adjusted near to the end of the magnet is a reed on which is mounted a diaphragm. The currents as they pass round the magnet affect its magnetism and consequently its pull on the reed, which vibrates according to the currents passing and communicates its vibrations to the diaphragm.

In the "moving coil" type, on the other hand (Figure 37 (*b*)) we have either a permanent magnet or an electro-magnet. The former are termed P.M. moving coil speakers; the latter are "energised", a special tapping on the mains transformer supplying the current, which when rectified energises the electro-magnet.

Round the central pole-piece of the magnet is a tiny coil of very thin wire, only a very narrow space being left between the two. This is the "speech coil" through which flow the currents at audio-frequency, and it is fixed to the loudspeaker diaphragm as shown in the sketch.

Between the pole-piece and the magnet there is obviously a strong magnetic field, and this must cut through the coils of the speech coil. This coil itself has also a magnetic field in consequence of the currents flowing through it, and the two fields react with one another. When the two fields oppose one another the magnet repels the coil; if they assist one another the magnet attracts the coil. The result is that the coil vibrates in the gap and carries the diaphragm with it, thus producing the corresponding sound waves.

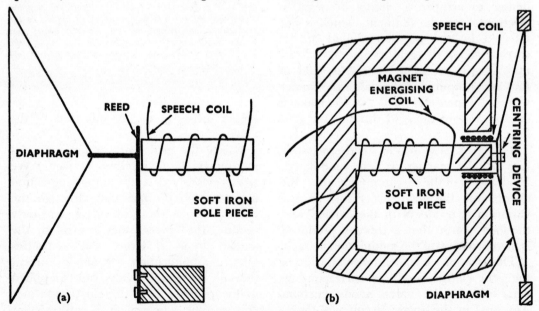

FIGURE 37. *Two types of loudspeaker, moving iron and moving coil. The moving iron type (a) consists of a coil wound on a permanent magnet which attracts or repulses a reed to which is attached the diaphragm. In the moving coil type, (b) the diaphragm is attached to a coil which in turn is attracted or repulsed by either a permanent or electro-magnet.*

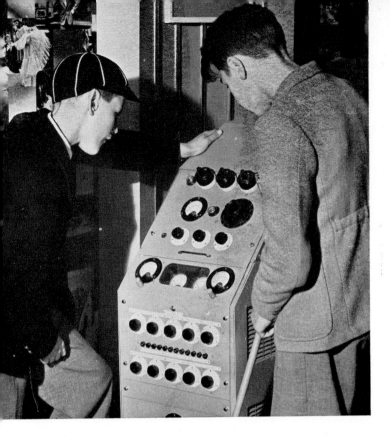

(Left) *Large screen television projector for use in cinemas.*

(Below) *Cinema cameras as used in the studio and out of doors.*

Television camera and controls; control room showing control desk, drive and phasing equipment and, through the window, the sound transmitter T2.A.

(Left) *Flexible cables connecting cameras to racks in control room.*

(Below) *Emitron television camera with cover removed, showing A. operating lever, B. first stage amplification, C. photo-electric mosaic screen behind lens, D. lens and, E. electric gun.*

(Left) *Broadcasting House installation of coaxial transmission equipment for the television link to the Crystal Palace. Left-hand bay: Two sets of transmitting equipment together with carrier test equipment. Right-hand bay: Two sets of receiving equipment.*

(Below) *Coaxial feeder switching equipment. Mimic diagram showing feeder switching positions on the wall at the right.*

Carrier modulator equipment, rear view with covers removed. Upper unit: Video amplifier and black level clamp. Lower unit: Carrier modulator.

Carrier demodulator equipment, rear view with covers removed. Right-hand side: Demodulator section. Left-hand side: Video amplifier.

CHAPTER V

THE ELECTRONIC EYE

Oₙᴇ of the most useful devices the electron has given to man is the photocell, introduced to you in Chapter II. The chief sphere for the photocell is industry, where not only can it be made to perform important operations without any human supervision at all, but where it can take the drudgery out of scores of soul-destroying tasks and perform them more rapidly and accurately than any man or woman, and where it can make safety of life and limb a certainty for the worker who has to perform otherwise dangerous tasks.

The photocell has often been described as the "electric eye" because it does seem to "see" things in an uncanny fashion. But there is a brain behind the eye which

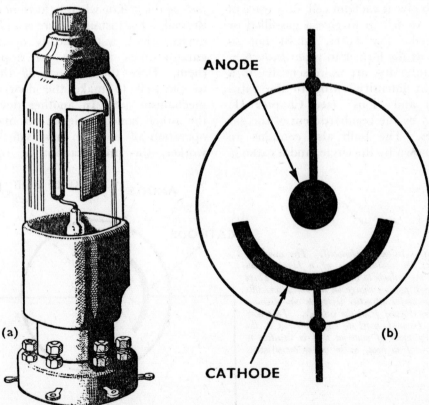

ANODE

CATHODE

Figure 38. *Photocell (a) as it really is and (b) as it usually is shown diagrammatically. The cathode in practice is a folder of thin metal made as large as possible to catch the light, while the anode consists of a loop of wire just in front of it.*

can *respond* to what the eye sees and, just as in the human case, can set motors working to perform specified operations.

The usual accompaniments of the photocell are the valve amplifier and the relay.

The job of the valve amplifier is to boost up the relatively tiny current flowing in the photocell until it is big enough to work the relay.

The job of the relay is simply that of a *switch*. The current flowing through it from the valve amplifier causes the relay to allow the flow of a much larger current —current generally sufficient to drive a small or large motor.

The conventional sign for a photocell is shown in Figure 38 (*b*). It consists of a glass bulb or tube, evacuated to a high degree to give a vacuum cell, or a trace of gas may be left in to give a gas-filled or "soft" cell. The latter, whilst not so sensitive as the former to rapid *fluctuations* of light intensity, are more sensitive to a *given* light intensity owing to the extra electrons and "ions" (see Chapter II) produced by the bombardment of the gas molecules. The bulb also contains an anode, shown by the circle, and a cathode

coated with a light-sensitive metal. In some cases the interior of the bulb itself is coated with this metal, a small "window" being left through which the light can fall on to the coating (Figure 38 (*a*)).

The action of the cell is as follows: Suppose anode and cathode are connected externally through a high-tension battery giving the former a high positive charge. Then, when light falls on the cathode (Figure 39) electrons will be shot out from it and will be attracted by the positively charged anode. Hence a "current in space" will be set up, completing the anode-cathode circuit round which a current of a few milliamperes will flow.

Now this small current may be required to perform an action either when light *falls on* the cell or when light is *cut off* from the cell. For instance, there is a photocell device which automatically opens your garage doors as your car approaches them. Here the car *cuts off* the light to the cell to make the door-opening mechanism act. In another device, on the other hand, designed to make the operation of a large press safe for the worker, the press cannot be operated

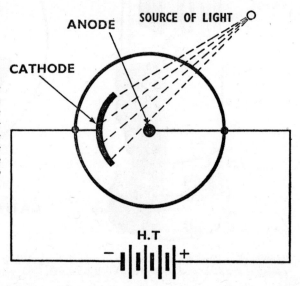

FIGURE 39. *Action of photocell. The anode is connected to the positive pole of a high tension battery and the cathode to the negative pole. There is thus a high positive charge on the anode and this gives it a powerful attractive force for any electrons that may be released from the cathode. This does not happen, however, until the light falls on it, the cathode being made of material that is sensitive to light instead of to heat, as in an ordinary valve.*

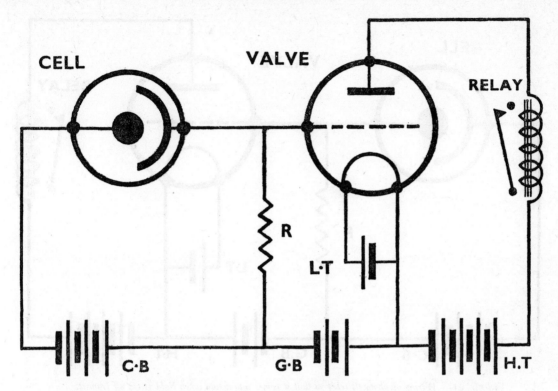

FIGURE 40. *Wiring of photocell relay so that it comes into action when light falls on the cell.*

so long as the worker's hand *blocks* the light falling on the cell. When his hand is *removed* the press works.

In either case, the components of the circuit are the same, but the connections to the photocell are reversed. Figures 40 and 41 show the two arrangements. In Figure 40 a current flows through the relay when the light falls on the cell; in Figure 41 current flows only when the normal illumination of the cell is cut off. Let us see what happens in each case.

From the first diagram we see that we have the anode of the cell connected to the cathode through (1) a H.T. battery and (2) a resistance. An amplifying valve is also connected with its grid and cathode to the resistance.

When no light reaches the cell no electrons are emitted. It acts like a gap

in the photocell side of the circuit, and the cell might as well not be there.

The grid of the valve is kept negative enough by the grid bias battery, G.B, so that little or no anode current flows in the valve and the relay does not function. As soon as light falls on the cell, electrons emitted by the cathode flow towards the anode—that is, away from the grid of the valve—leaving the latter positively charged. The function of the resistance, R, which is large, is to prevent this charge disappearing again. With the grid thus positively charged, the anode current in the valve increases, and the relay comes into action. Suppose, however, we wish to operate in the reverse manner, i.e. with the cell normally illuminated, and interruption of the light bringing the relay into operation. Then we simply reverse the

65

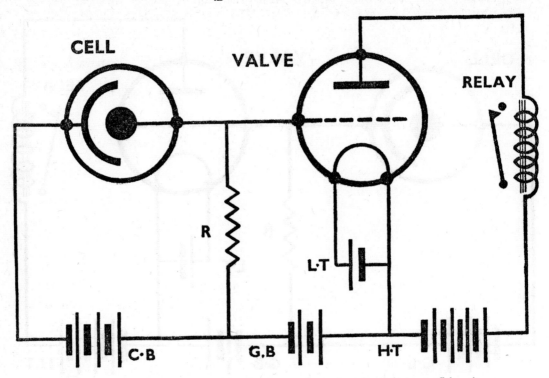

FIGURE 41.   *Wiring of photocell relay so that it comes into action when light is cut off from it.*

connections to the cell, as shown in Figure 41. In this case, with light falling on the cell, electrons flow from cathode to anode, and hence to the grid of the valve, charging it negatively. This negative charge, together with that provided by the grid bias battery, prevents the current flowing in the valve. When the light is cut off, the grid bias battery is left on its own, and as its voltage is arranged to be small this time, enough current now flows in the anode circuit to trip the relay.

The relay can take several forms, but its function is always the same: it acts as a *switch*, the current from the valve amplifier setting in motion a much larger current, e.g. that in the "mains". There are two main classes of relay: the "solenoid" and the gas-filled relay or "thyratron" which we met in Chapter II.

The principle of the solenoid is exactly that of the electric bell except that the use we make of it is different. It consists essentially of a bar of soft iron round which a coil of wire is wound. The wire, of course, is insulated carefully from the bar. When a current—say, that from the amplifying valve—passes through the coil, it produces a magnetic field, which causes the bar to become temporarily magnetized. This attracts the contact (Figure 42), which closes the mains circuit and causes the motor to operate. Notice carefully that there is no connection between the valve circuit and the mains circuit.

The gas-filled relay or thyratron has already been mentioned in Chapter II and will be found useful again in Chapter VI where we deal with television scanning circuits. This valve has the property of being switched on suddenly by the re-

66

duction of negative grid bias, and it will continue to operate in spite of what happens to the grid thereafter until the anode current is definitely switched off. Thus we can see that it is just the thing we require for working with photocells.

The application of the gas-filled relay in conjunction with the photocell is well demonstrated in the job of automatic counting. There are in industry machines which fill cans or bottles or packets at very high speeds, feeding the filled containers to a travelling belt which takes them to the next operation. What a fatiguing job it would be for an operator who had to stand by the side of the conveyor and count the packages! It is done very simply, however, by the photocell.

On one side of the conveyor we fix a light source with its beam directed across the belt to a photocell on the other side. When a package passes the beam of light is interrupted, and we require this interruption to be *recorded* on a counter something like the mileage counter on a bicycle.

We therefore set up an arrangement something like that shown in Figure 43.

When light falls on the cell, i.e. when no package blocks its path, the thyratron relay is kept out of operation because the combined action of the grid bias battery and the photocell give its grid a large negative bias. Immediately the path of the light is blocked, however, the cell is cut out of circuit and there is a large reduction in the negative bias on the grid of the thyratron. This brings the thyratron into action. It passes a large anode current immediately, and this anode current, passing round the solenoid, attracts the contact, which is normally held away from it by a spring. The action of attracting the arm of the contact may be made to bring forward a ratchet which turns the drum of the counter, and at the same time it can be made to *break* the current in the anode circuit as soon as this has been done. This makes the device re-set itself as soon as the passage of one packet has been recorded and leaves the apparatus free to go through the same operations for the next.

Sufficient has been said, I think, to indicate to you roughly the way in which the "magic eye" can be put to work. Now let me describe some interesting applications of the photocell, remembering always that the cell itself only generates a weak impulse that is amplified and then made to actuate a switch (relay) that starts the actual *working current* in motion.

In the first place, the whole principle of the talking picture depends on the photo-

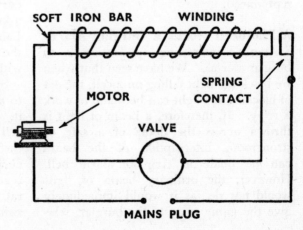

FIGURE 42. *Solenoid method of working photocell relay circuit. A solenoid is a bar of soft iron which is turned into a magnet when an electric current is allowed to flow in the wire that is coiled round it—in other words, an electro-magnet. The bar is close enough to a spring contact to attract the contact when it becomes magnetized and so close the relay circuit. Thus a current is caused to flow in the latter and perform any operation required.*

SOFT IRON BAR   WINDING

SPRING CONTACT

MOTOR

VALVE

MAINS PLUG

cell, both in taking the picture and in presenting it. Briefly it is this:

Speech and music are transmitted to the ear by sound waves. These sound waves are a form of energy and can be made to vibrate the diaphragm of a microphone. The vibration of the microphone diaphragm alters the pressure it exerts on the carbon granules behind it, and each alteration in pressure means a change in the electrical resistance of the carbon.

If a current is sent through the carbon, therefore, it will vary in tune with the sound waves that are striking the microphone. Now this varying current is made to vary the current sent through a powerful lamp focused on the edge of the strip of celluloid on which the picture is being taken, so that the edge of the strip when the film is developed shows a large number of gradations of light and shade.

In the projection room, the "light track" becomes the "sound track". Light transmitted through it is focused on to the window of a photocell. Then, just as the strength of the light falling on the photocell varies according to the differing shades of the sound track, so the strength of the current passed by the cell varies, and if this varying current is applied to the loudspeakers behind the screen the original sound which produced the track will be reproduced.

A Photocell works a Burglar Alarm

Another interesting application is to burglar alarms. We have seen that when we block the light falling on a cell, the act of blocking the light can be made to work a relay. If, therefore, a beam of light is thrown across the doors of a safe or strongroom, interruption of the beam can be made to ring an alarm bell. However, the ordinary beam of light would not do, as it would immediately give the game away to the burglar, who

could take steps to put the alarm out of action before he proceeded to work.

Such burglar alarms, therefore, make use of a type of light that is not visible as a beam. It lies just beyond the red end of the spectrum amongst the heat rays. Not all photo-electric cells are sensitive to these rays, but those with cathodes coated with the metal caesium are sensitive, and work quite well with them. Burglar alarms of this type will give instant warning of the presence of a burglar and will ring an alarm bell either within the building or even at the police station.

Photocells are much used nowadays in "pyrometry", i.e. the measurement of heat, at very much higher levels than can be used with the ordinary type of thermometer. This is the case, for instance, with the electric furnace. Hot metal sends out infra-red rays which are invisible to the naked eye, but which can be observed by the photocell whose cathode is coated with caesium. The hotter the metal, the more intense the infra-red rays sent out, and as current in the photocell is proportional to the intensity of light falling on the cathode, the current provides a useful measuring stick for temperature. All that is done is to include a suitable current meter in the photocell circuit and to graduate this meter not in units of current, but in temperatures, starting from a known temperature—say, 1,000 degrees Fahrenheit—and proceeding upwards at the same rate as infra-red intensity varies with temperature.

Such pyrometers can be made not only to *measure* temperature. They can *control* it. All that is necessary is to connect the cell in circuit with a thyratron and adjust the latter so that it just commences to pass current when the current from the cell reaches a certain value. Then the thyratron current can be made to work a switch, cutting off the current to the furnace and even operating a device for withdrawing the hot metal.

A final example of the use of infra-red with the photocell concerns the amount of smoke which factory chimneys are allowed to discharge by law. This may not be above a permitted density except at certain periods, and it would be a laborious sort of job to attempt to control the smoke going up the stack by human labour. The photocell does it automatically.

What is done is to pass a portion of the smoke going up the stack through a special pipe. This pipe is provided with two windows, one on each side, and a beam of infra-red light is passed across the smoke stream to a photocell. According to the density of the smoke, so the current in the photocell varies, and things can be so adjusted that when it reaches a certain degree of blackness, i.e. when the light is cut off to a certain degree, machinery comes into operation to shut off the black smoke, or an alarm indicator can convey the information to the stoker on duty.

Other Industrial Uses of Photocells

Another type of photocell in common use is what is known as the barrier or rectifier cell. A common form of this consists of a small plate of iron—say, one inch square—on one side of which is deposited a very thin layer of the substance selenium. If we now connect a meter to the two sides of the cell and allow light to fall on the selenium side we will get a current of electrons recorded. These electrons are produced by the light where the selenium meets the iron, and that is why we had to make the layer of selenium very

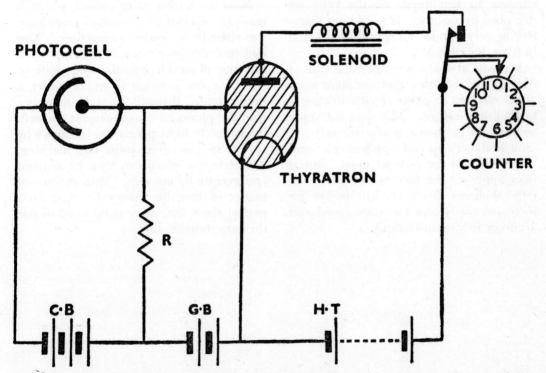

FIGURE 43. *Gas-filled or thyratron valve used in photocell circuit. This valve has the property of being switched on merely by the reduction of negative grid bias, and is shown here in a circuit suitable for controlling the repetitive operation of counting.*

thin in order to let the light in. We call it a barrier or rectifier cell because the electrons are made to flow in one direction only. A plate of copper with a thin layer of red oxide on it will also show the same effect.

The great advantage of this type of cell is that it works without any external battery at all, converting the light energy directly into electric current. It is in fact its own battery. It is also small in size, and not easily damaged, and is thus very suitable for any case where we want a small cell that we can carry around, such as in an exposure meter for photography.

The barrier type of cell can, of course, also be used for many of the applications mentioned before, but it is not quite as sensitive to small amounts of light, nor does it respond as well to very rapid changes in brightness, as the cells we described previously. It would not therefore be very suitable for sound production in films, for example.

We said at the outset, and the title of our chapter indicates, that the main work of the electron in photo-electric devices is to abolish drudgery. This does not apply so much to the home, where the cell will only find very special applications—and those will not be general ones. But it does apply to the factory, where it not only abolishes drudgery, but makes for increased safety and for more speed and accuracy in vital operations.

For the electron can be made to count things and to measure them; it can be made to reject faulty articles; it can be made to reject substandard objects from conveyor belts, to open and shut valves as required, to empty and fill tanks, to start motors and stop them. I can only give you here one or two examples of the way in which it is making itself of use to industry.

One remarkable example concerns the making of tin-plate for the cans and containers so much of our food is packed in today. Tin-plate is rolled out in wide sheets at very high speeds by special machines, and it is vital that there should be no pin-holes in the sheet, or the resulting cans would not be air-tight. If they are not air-tight the consumer runs the risk of getting food poisoning.

Now the testing of this sheet, which is made in rolls many hundreds of yards long, was virtually impossible at one time. You had to make your tin, and then test that. But the photocell has changed matters. As the sheet is made it passes under a bright light. Beneath the sheet there is a special photocell arrangement which, immediately light penetrates the sheet by reason of pin-holes, stops the machine. The defective place can then be marked and eventually cut out. Thus the actual maker of the tins knows he receives a perfect sheet and there is no need to test the cans individually.

CHAPTER VI

THINGS OUT OF SIGHT

ONE OF the most difficult jobs undertaken by the electron in the whole of his short career has been that whereby he now enables men to see things out of sight. To this new art we have applied the word "Television", and in the present chapter I shall try to show you what the problems he encountered were, and how he overcame them. Incidentally, I should be able to give you a fair idea of how television works.

The electron was lucky in that, to some extent, the ground had been prepared for him, and to a like extent I have prepared it for you in previous chapters. As a matter of fact, there already existed the cinematograph, the radio, the photocell and the cathode ray tube; and it was by taking some ideas from the cinematograph and radio, and applying them in a new way with the help of the cell and the tube, that the problem of seeing things out of sight was eventually solved.

When it comes to "seeing" things, the very last instrument to be brought into play is the *eye*. You can't go beyond that, whether you are using a microscope or a telescope; whether you are watching a cinema picture or the image on a television screen. Now the eye has certain peculiarities, strange tricks that you would not suspect unless you were told about them, and we have been able to develop the cinema picture and television simply because it has proved possible to make use of one of these tricks in a novel and entertaining way.

The peculiarity to which I refer here is that known as "visual persistence", which simply means that the eye will continue to see an object for a small fraction of a second after all light has been cut off from it. I could give you numerous examples of this persistence, but here is just one which you will often have noticed yourself.

Suppose, on a very dark night, a man walking some distance in front of you down the road throws away the end of a lighted cigarette. What do you "see"? You *see* a bright "arc" of light, a "streak" running from the man's hand to the ground. But what did you really see? You saw a single bright spot of light in a succession of different positions. That is all.

What happened, of course, was that the image of the spot in one position *persists* in the eye for a fraction of a second; but during that fraction the spot has actually moved on to a new position. So the eye records a bright line joining the two spots. And this goes on all the way down to the ground, where the spot remains stationary.

The fact is that the images the eye observes are actually recorded on the *retina* at the back of the eye by chemical changes which take place in the millions of cells composing it. These cells, however, take an appreciable fraction of a second to return to normal and as a result one sees an object for a fraction of a second after it has been taken away.

This fraction is about one-tenth of a second.
How is "visual persistence" made use of

1	2	3	4	5	6	7	8
9	10	11	12	13	14	15	16
17	18	19	20	21	22	23	24
25	26	27	28	29	30	31	32
33	34	35	36	37	38	39	40
41	42	43	44	45	46	47	48

FIGURE 44. *These numbered squares give some idea of what happens in the scanning of the screen in a television camera. The principle is to illuminate the whole screen so that we see it as a complete picture, but in order to make the picture suitable for transmission each tiny portion has to be illuminated in rotation. Because the eye sees things for a fraction of a second after they have actually moved, it is possible to let a thin beam of light travel rapidly from one square to the next and yet to leave the impression that all the squares are illuminated at once.*

in the cinema? When you watch a cinema picture you *appear* to see a continuously changing scene. But what do you really see? You see a "still" picture as it might be from a lantern slide, projected on to the screen. It remains so projected for a fraction of a second. Then it vanishes, and for another fraction of a second the screen is blank. At the end of the blank period another "still" flashes out on the screen, but this time the position of things in the scene have *altered* slightly.

But, during the blank period the image of the *first* "still" persists on the eye's retina, so that by the time the second, slightly altered "still" takes its place, you have no idea at all that there has been any gap. The images flow one after the other into your mind in continuous succession, so that finally you get the impression of unbroken motion.

Cinema images change at the rate of twenty-four per second. That means that during one second's run of the film, twenty-four separate images, each slightly different from the rest, are presented to the eye, and because of "visual persistence" these blend into one smooth-flowing, moving "scene" without causing you any discomfort.

Speed at which the Picture is made

The electron, in devising his television system, borrowed from the cinema this technique of presenting to the eye a rapid succession of images, relying on the "persistence" of one image for a fraction of a second *to enable him to prepare his next image.*

For this is where the problem which confronted the electron differs fundamentally from that confronting the cinematograph engineer. Whereas the latter has his next picture all ready on a strip of celluloid, the television engineer has to *build up* his picture from a series of tiny dots *all in the short space of one-twenty-fifth of a second.*

You probably know that an ordinary printed picture in a book or newspaper is made up of tiny dots. In any case, a magnifying glass will enable you to pick out these dots for yourself, and you will see how dots of different depths of blackness make up the light and shade in the picture.

Let us forget about light and shade for a moment. Suppose we have a screen of ground glass like that in the back of the portrait photographer's camera. We sit in front of this in a dark room, and behind the camera we have an arrangement which will focus a small, square spot of light anywhere within the boundaries of the screen (Figure 44).

Suppose, further, that our arrangement allows the spot to start at square 1, travel to square 8, return *instantaneously* to square 9, travel to square 16, return (instantaneously again) to square 17, and so on, until the whole screen has been traversed and we end up at square 48.

If, at first, the spot travels slowly, we shall be able to follow it, but as we speed it up our old friend "visual persistence"

gradually comes into play. The image of square 1 will "persist" for about one-tenth of a second, so that if the speed is such that it takes one-tenth of a second for the spot to travel from square 1 to square 8 we shall appear to see a white band in the first position (Figure 45).

What happens with Greater Speed

The spot travels instantaneously, however, back to square 9. This first band persists no longer, but for the next one-tenth of a second we shall appear to see a band in the second position. This band,

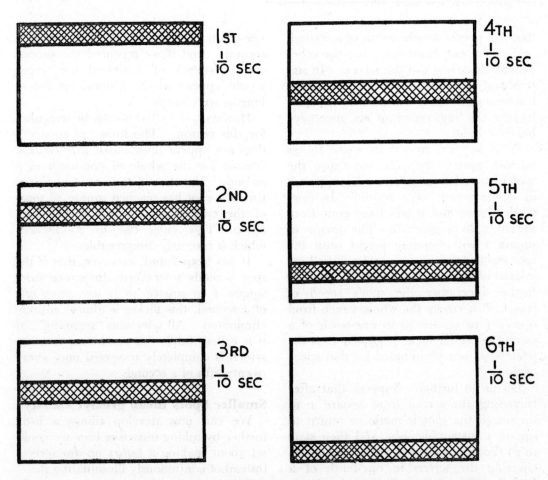

FIGURE 45. *The shaded bands across these rectangles show what happens when the spot which illuminates each square in Fig. 46 is speeded up in its movement so that it covers a whole line of squares in one-tenth of a second.*

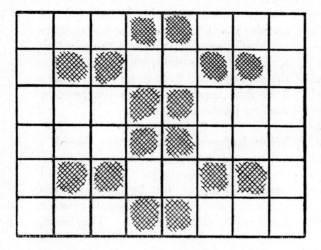

FIGURE 46. *This is the beginning of the formation of a picture on the screen of a television camera. All pictures in black and white consist merely of irregular areas of light and shade, and the drawing suggests that the spot which is illuminating each square in turn meets something that causes it to light up some squares with less intensity than others. When the movement of the spot of light is very rapid, the screen appears to be illuminated by a steady picture, in spite of the fact that each spot is lighted in turn.*

too, will persist for one-tenth of a second, and so on, one band following the other instantaneously down the screen. In six-tenths of a second, therefore, the screen has been completely traversed by the spot, leaving the impression of six successive bands of light.

What happens now if we speed things up still more? Suppose we cause the spot to travel from square 1 to square 8 in one-twentieth of a second. In one-tenth of a second it will have gone from square 1 to square 16. The image of square 1 will therefore persist until the spot reaches that square, and we shall see a band of light *two* rows broad. And by further increasing the spot's speed of travel till it covers the whole screen from square 1 to square 48 in one-tenth of a second we could make it appear that the *whole screen* was illuminated for that space of time.

Let us go further. Suppose that after traversing the screen from square 1 to square 48 the spot is made to return to square 1 instantaneously, and then start to go through its former operations again, covering the screen in one-tenth of a second. Our screen will then appear to be continuously illuminated for two times

one-tenth of a second, i.e. one-fifth of a second. And if we repeated the process *every* one-tenth of a second the screen would appear wholly illuminated for as long as we wished.

However, the effect would be irregular, for this reason. The image of square 1 does not appear illuminated *with the same intensity* for the whole of one-tenth of a second. The effect dies away, and by the time the spot has reached square 48 some of the earlier squares are almost dark again. This gives rise to a "flicker" which is intensely disagreeable.

It has been found, however, that if the spot is made to traverse the screen from square 1 to square 48 in *one twenty-fifth* of a second, this flicker is almost entirely eliminated. All television "scanning", as it is called, fulfils this condition, that the screen is completely traversed once every twenty-fifth of a second.

Smaller Spots mean greater Clarity

We can now develop things a little further by asking ourselves how we could set about making a *pattern* on our screen, instead of continuously illuminating it.

Suppose, when the spot came to certain squares (Figure 46), a shutter comes into

FIGURE 47. *This is not a puzzle picture, but an actual representation, many times enlarged, of the way a picture can be built up on the television screen by a series of dots, the dots being tiny areas illuminated by greater or lesser degrees of light. In the actual screen, of course, the dots would have varying weights of tone; that is to say, they would not be all the same strength of blackness; but even with this plain black-and-white drawing a surprising effect can be obtained by viewing the picture at a distance of about fifteen feet.*

Try it by standing the book up on the table and walking away from it. All of a sudden the squares will turn into a picture.

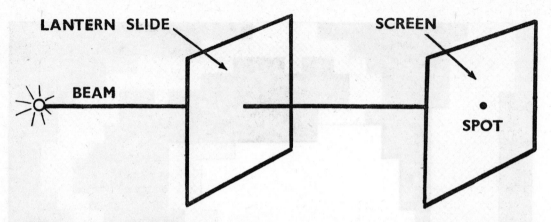

FIGURE 48. *Frosted glass screen with beam of light focused upon it through a lantern slide. As the beam of light moves to and fro the various parts of the picture on the slide—transparent, of course—interfere with the intensity of the light, and the beam traces a similar picture on the screen.*

operation, shutting off the light altogether. Since no light ever reaches the screen when the spot is in these positions a *pattern* something like a crossword puzzle diagram will appear on the screen.

With a spot of light one forty-eighth the size of the whole screen, however, pattern-making possibilities are obviously limited; but as we *decrease the size of the spot* the possibilities grow infinitely greater. In fact, by stopping out the light over the appropriate squares, it is possible to get the sort of black-and-white picture shown in Figure 47. It does not require much insight to see that if we reduce our light spot to a mere *point*, infinitely greater detail could be obtained in our final picture.

However, the picture remains a black-and-white one. There are only two shades in it—pure white and dead black. What are the possibilities of securing *gradations of tone* as in a photograph or a half-tone illustration? Obviously, this would require a much more complicated arrangement at the back of our screen. The spot of light on its way to the screen could, for instance, be made to traverse a

lantern slide, as in Figure 48. Suppose this shows a ship in full sail.

A lantern slide is the "positive" of a photographic negative. If you think a moment, you will see clearly that a "negative" would not do, since it would give a reversed picture on our screen.

In one twenty-fifth of a second our spot of light traverses the whole area of the lantern slide. But if we divide our slide up into a very large number of small areas each the size of our spot it is clear that the intensity of the light which gets through the slide will vary from element to element, according to the thickness of the film on the slide.

The intensity of the spot which falls on the screen will therefore vary in accordance with the light and shade in the picture on the lantern slide, and what we shall now see on the screen is not just a plain rectangle of white light, but a *reproduction* of the picture on the slide.

Our picture, however, is a "still" picture, i.e. the *same* picture is reproduced on the screen twenty-five times every second, giving the impression that the screen is being illuminated continuously

76

through the slide. If, by some means, we could move into place at the expiration of a twenty-fifth of a second a new slide showing the ship in a slightly different position, and, after exposing that slide for a twenty-fifth of a second, replace it with a third showing the ship in a still different position, and so on, we should eventually get the impression of *motion*.

To sum up. We have found that, using a simple spot of light and a ground-glass screen it is possible, first, to build up a "still" picture with full light and shade effects, and second, to produce in such a picture the idea of motion. The essential things are as follows:

(1) That the spot of light is capable of being moved over the screen in a horizontal and a vertical direction, covering successively every point on it.

(2) That one complete traverse of the screen is made in one twenty-fifth of a second.

(3) That the intensity of the spot can be varied continuously according to the light and shade in the original "still" picture which is being reproduced.

(4) That individual "stills" can be changed each twenty-fifth of a second so that the idea of motion is imparted to whatever is viewed.

Cathode Ray Tube and Photocell again

Those are the basic problems which confront the television engineer, and we have now to see how, with the aid of the cathode ray tube and the photocell, he has been able to solve them. For convenience we shall first see how the actual television picture being transmitted is "built up" again from a series of wireless waves. Then we shall see how such a picture can be transmitted in the form of wireless waves. Finally, we shall be able to see transmitter and receiver working together.

The purely imaginary set-up which we have been using to show the principle of "scanning" used in television consisted of a ground-glass plate, viewed in a dark room, behind which was a source of light concentrated into a beam which fell on the back of the plate. This appeared to the observer as a bright spot of light on a

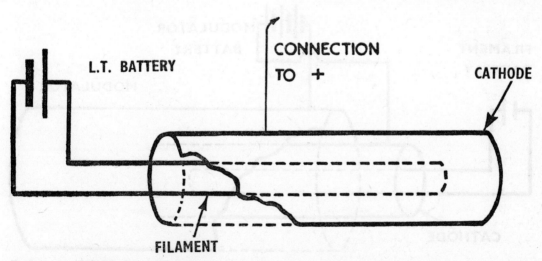

FIGURE 49. *Indirectly heated cathode of cathode ray tube. It is possible to make the filament behave as the cathode, but the better principle is to have the two separate, so that the cathode, shown here as a tubular cover over the filament, is independent of the heating current. This makes for a much steadier flow of electrons.*

plate and we presumed that by purely mechanical means the spot could be made to move to and fro across the plate, or up and down it, thus being capable of illuminating any particular place on the plate we liked. Finally, we supposed that the intensity of the spot—its brightness or otherwise—could be controlled at will.

How the Brilliance of the Light Spot is varied

In the cathode ray tube we have the end wall of the tube forming a fluorescent screen. At the other end of the tube we have an electron "gun" capable of firing a narrow "pencil" of electrons directly at the screen, the point where the pencil hits the screen appearing as a tiny, glowing spot. Then we have our two anodes to attract and focus the electrons, and finally we have two pairs of electrically charged plates (or in some cases two sets of electromagnetic coils), by which we can deflect the course of the electron beam in either a horizontal or a vertical direction.

So far, however, one thing is lacking. This is some device for varying the *intensity* of the fluorescent spot, making it light or dark, or even blotting it out altogether.

You will remember from our first description of the cathode ray tube in Chapter II that the source of electrons was the usual type of "indirectly heated cathode". This consists (Figure 49) of a cylinder of suitably-coated metal inside which is a wire filament heated by a separate battery. The heat from the glowing filament heats up the cathode after a few seconds, and it commences to emit electrons in the usual way.

Now in the cathode ray tube as used in television receivers we place a small cylinder of metal, known as a "modulator" or "grid", round the cathode (Figure 50). This grid is made to have a *negative* charge by connecting it to the negative pole of the small battery, the cathode itself being connected to the *positive* pole of this battery. The grid is now negative and will *repel* the electrons as they come off the cathode, just like the grid of a valve.

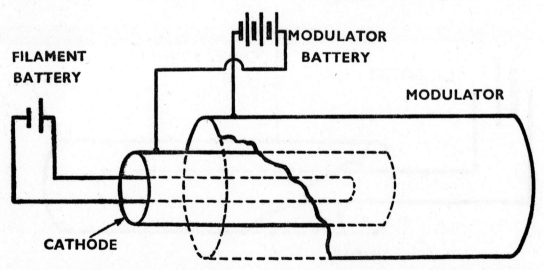

FIGURE 50. *Not only is the cathode of the cathode ray tube independent of the filament which carries the heating current, but it usually has a further refinement in a modulator, which covers the cathode and acts in a way similar to the grid of a valve.*

Carrier equaliser, rear view with covers removed.
Right-hand side: Variable attenuator.   Centre: Fixed attenuation and delay equalizers.   Left-hand side: Bode equalizer.

Carrier Amplifier, rear view with cover removed.   This is one of three amplifiers used in the coaxial transmission system.

General view of a telerecording suite, showing control desk, three film cameras with mechau drums, three display units, sound channel and video channel.

Mechau continuous motion telerecording equipment, picture display unit on the left, behind it are the vision amplifier and power supply cabinets.

Flying spot mechau telecine machine installed at the television studios. This system was devised by the BBC engineering staff. The scanning tube which produces the flying spot can just be seen through the open inspection door situated near the middle of the apparatus bay. The multiplier photo-electric cell is visible just to the left of the top motor control rod.

General view of a 35mm. suppressed frame television recording assembly. The oscilloscope on the left is used for monitoring the peak white brightness of the recording display tube. In the centre is the camera unit and on the right the sound recording equipment.

General view of a magnetic film recording channel temporarily installed in a van. This channel is used for recording high quality sound for the Television Film Unit.

Television camera.

Television camera with a zoom lens which acts as a telescope and magnifies the matter to be photographed. It is used for close-up work, for outside broadcasts, in the studio and in theatres where it is inconvenient to use the camera near to the stage.

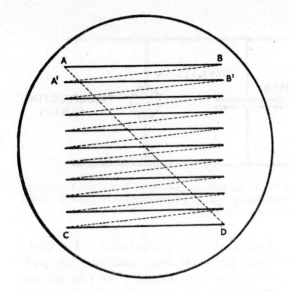

FIGURE 51. *When the beam of electrons in the cathode ray tube is moved rapidly over the screen it obviously takes a certain time to move back from the end of one line to the beginning of the next. Such movement is of no use for scanning purposes, and is consequently arranged to take place as rapidly as possible. Some idea of the speed of the movement can be gained from the fact that it takes no more than one twenty-fifth of a second to scan the whole picture! In this drawing the backward movements of the spot of light are shown by dotted lines. Starting at A it would move to B, then return almost instantly to A_1 on the line below. Arriving at the bottom, D, it would flash back instantly to A, and the whole process would begin all over again.*

How the Screen becomes Dark or Bright

We now have a means of varying the intensity of the electron beam. All we have to do is to arrange to vary the negative charge on the modulator or grid. The more negative it is, the fewer will be the electrons passing out to the anodes, and hence the dimmer the spot. With the grid very negative, scarcely any electrons will reach the anode, and the screen will be dark.

Let us sum up again before going ahead. First, as we saw in Chapter II and from Figure 15, we can move the electron beam *sideways* by varying the charge on the first pair of deflecting plates. Second, we can move the beam *up or down* by varying the charge on the second pair of deflecting plates. Third, we can vary the *intensity* of the beam (and consequently the brightness of the fluorescent spot) by varying the strength of the negative charge on the modulator or shield.

It would appear, therefore, that we have everything necessary to copy with our cathode ray tube all the operations we carried out with our imaginary apparatus

in the dark room. But several important considerations remain. The first of these concerns the path traced by the spot, and this leads us to the vital question of "scanning".

Scanning with the Cathode Ray Tube

In our original set-up we imagined our spot of light starting at the left-hand top corner of the ground-glass plate and moving horizontally across it to the top right-hand corner. Then we imagined it moving back *instantaneously* to a spot just a shade *below* its starting-point, whence it again traversed the plate horizontally to a point just below where it ended its first line. Then the process recommenced and was continued until the spot ended up in the bottom right-hand corner of the plate. Arrived at that point, it had to jump back, again simultaneously, to its first starting-point, after which the whole series of operations was gone through again.

We saw, moreover, that if these processes were carried out so that the whole journey between A and D (Figure 51) were completed not less than twenty-five

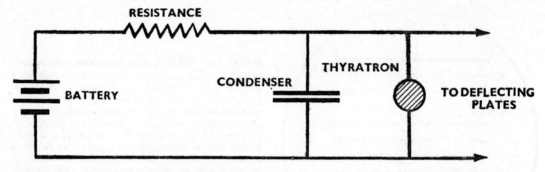

FIGURE 52. *Wiring connections for deflecting plates in a cathode ray tube or oscilloscope. In this circuit a thyratron valve is used because it has the ability to build up a large current rapidly when the positive charge on the anode is sufficient to overcome the negative charge on the grid.*

times per second, the resulting impression on a viewer would be one of continuous illumination of the rectangle ABCD.

How are we to do this with the cathode ray tube?

Let us consider first how we shall move the spot from A to B. Clearly, we shall need steadily to increase the charge on the vertical pair of plates in our cathode ray tube, and when we reach the spot B we need to *discharge* the plates automatically, so that the spot swings *almost instantaneously* back to A. (In reality, of course, it will not swing back to A, but to A¹, a little below A. This is taken care of by the horizontal plates, as will be explained later.)

Now one way of building up a charge of electricity is to use a *condenser*. You can imagine a condenser as a *tank* or *reservoir*, and the electricity as the water which pours into it. Our tank, however, has to be fitted with a sort of hinged bottom, so that when the time comes the bottom can be opened and the tank emptied almost instantaneously.

So we set up the sort of circuit shown in Figure 52. The condenser is connected to a battery through a large resistance. This resistance acts like a constriction or "block" in a water pipe. It *hinders* the flow of the electricity, just as a constriction

hinders the flow of the water. The effect here is to fill the condenser up with electricity very slowly. We can control the rate as we please through the actual value we choose for the resistance.

Clearly, then, if the condenser is now connected to the vertical pair of deflecting plates, the charge on them will grow along with the growing charge of electricity in the condenser, and the spot will move horizontally across the fluorescent screen at a speed depending on the rate at which we charge the condenser, i.e. on the size of the resistance. Moreover, if we had some arrangement which would *discharge* the condenser when the spot reached the point B, the operation would recommence. We should thus obtain a series of relatively slow and steady charges, followed by a rapid discharge.

Fortunately, we have at our disposal just the thing for rapidly discharging the condenser. This is our old friend the *thyratron* valve described in Chapter II.

As we saw in that chapter, the construction of the valve is such that, with a small negative charge on the grid, no current flows until the charge on the *anode* has reached a certain critical value. When, however, that critical value has been reached, a current starts to flow and builds up very rapidly to a high value.

These are just the conditions we require, so we connect a thyratron as shown in Figure 52. As the condenser slowly fills up, so the charge on the anode of the thyratron increases, until the critical point is reached and current begins to flow in the valve. This grows so quickly that the thyratron almost immediately becomes nothing more or less than a short-circuit over the two terminals of the condenser, and the latter is thus discharged.

Now the point at which current begins to flow in the thyratron is determined by the value of the negative charge on the grid, and we can adjust this to just such a value as brings the horizontal traverse of the spot to a stop at point B.

More or less the same arrangement can be adopted to ensure that the spot starts a new line a little below its starting-point, A. Here the *horizontal* pair of deflecting plates comes into play. The only difference is that the charging of the condenser goes on at a much slower rate. The time taken by the vertical travel is equal to the time which we allot for the picture, i.e. one twenty-fifth of a second, whilst the time taken for the horizontal travel must be shorter than this by the number of lines we require. If we want 400 lines, then the time of travel from one side of the screen to the other would have to be one-ten-thousandth of a second. This interval, small as it is, is well within the capabilities of modern apparatus.

How varying Signal builds up Picture

We now find ourselves in a position to build up a picture on the fluorescent screen of our cathode ray tube provided some sort of signal is received which can be fed to the "modulator" in the tube. This signal, by varying the strength of the negative charge on the modulator, will increase or decrease the intensity of the light spot on our tube perhaps 500 times while it is scanning one line, and in the twinkling of an eye—one-twenty-fifth of a second, to be precise—will build up a picture in which light and shade are given full play.

Our next concern, therefore, lies at the

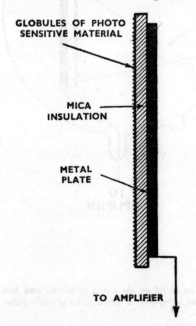

GLOBULES OF PHOTO SENSITIVE MATERIAL

MICA INSULATION

METAL PLATE

TO AMPLIFIER

FIGURE 53. *Photocell mosaic used as screen in the television camera. The screen of such a camera has to be broken up into tiny dots, each dot acting as a separate photo-electric cell. This is arranged for quite simply by means of a back plate of metal covered with mica insulation, on the front of which is a solution of photo-sensitive material so placed that it becomes a mass of tiny globules. This photo-sensitive material gives off electrons according to the intensity of the light that falls on it—more from the light areas of the picture than from the dark—and consequently each tiny globule becomes positively charged in greater or lesser degree. When the beam of negative electrons falls on them, therefore, they are discharged one after the other like condensers, causing variations of current in the metal plate at the back. Thus the metal plate can send impulses of varying intensity through the ether in proper rotation, and these impulses can be built up at the other end into the same picture that sent them on their journey.*

transmitting end of a television service, and we must answer the question: how can we produce such a signal?

The really wonderful instrument found at the transmitting end of all television transmitting systems is called an "Iconoscope" and is the invention of Dr. Zworykin, at present one of the leading technicians of the Radio Corporation of America. We shall meet him again later when we investigate the Electron Microscope.

The Iconoscope owes its development to the photocell and includes a scanning arrangement exactly like that found in a television receiver.

To refresh your memory, let me remind you that a photocell is a type of valve in which a beam of light liberates electrons from a cathode. These are drawn across to the anode because the latter is charged positively and so exerts a considerable attractive force on the negatively charged electrons. In the photocell proper this sets up a current in the anode-cathode circuit. This current is strictly proportional to the amount of light falling on the cell.

The principal feature of the Iconoscope is what is called a photocell "mosaic". Actually it consists, as shown in Figure 53, of more than a million very tiny globules of a photo-sensitive material, silver activated with caesium, evenly spaced over the surface of a sheet of mica. Behind the mica is a metal plate which has a con-

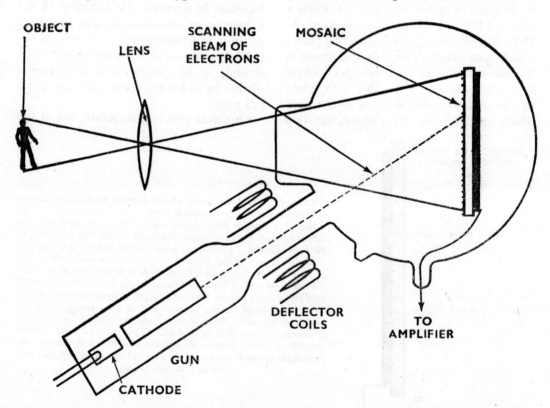

FIGURE 54. *How the lens of the television camera focuses the image of an object on the screen inside it, and how the electron gun and its beam of electrons then "scans" this light image and transforms it into a series of radio-pulses for transmission.*

nection through the glass bulb in which the mosaic is sealed.

The photo-sensitive material gives off electrons when light falls on it, and the number of electrons given off is proportional to the intensity of the light. Each globule of the mosaic is, in fact, the cathode of a tiny photo-electric cell.

Now comes a most important point. If a substance *gives off* electrons, this must leave the substance positively charged; but if we direct a stream of electrons on to the now positively charged globule, these will counteract the positive charge and will restore the neutral condition. This is as good as saying the cell is discharged again. Besides this, the globule, mica insulation, and metal plate form nothing more or less than a minute condenser, so that changes in the charge on the globule are faithfully reproduced in the plate, which, as we have said, is connected to the circuit outside the bulb.

Now look at Figure 54 which represents the Iconoscope in graphical fashion.

Just as in the ordinary camera, we have a lens which forms an image of the scene at which it is pointed, but instead of forming this image on a sensitised photographic plate, *it forms it on the photocell mosaic*. What does this mean?

It means that *at any instant* each tiny photocell of the mosaic is receiving an amount of light exactly proportional to that coming from the spot in the scene itself to which it corresponds. Each will therefore acquire a charge proportional to the amount of light at that point.

We now scan the mosaic with an electron beam which moves from side to side in a series of lines just as it does in the receiving tube. When the beam reaches each individual cell in turn it discharges it and leaves it ready to receive a fresh positive charge—which may be of different strength if the intensity of the light in that part of the scene to which it corresponds has undergone any change. Any change in the charge on the globules will, of course, be faithfully reflected in the charge on the plate connected to the external circuit of the transmitter.

How Vision Signals are Transmitted

Thus we have in the external circuit a continuously varying voltage, which is the very voltage we require to apply to the modulator of the cathode ray tube in the receiver. If this voltage *is* so applied, and if the image is being scanned by the Iconoscope in exactly the same way as the screen of our cathode ray tube is being scanned, then the intensity of the beam of electrons in the latter will vary in exactly the same way as does the light from each element of the scene to which the Iconoscope is directed.

We have now achieved television, provided it is possible to transmit by wireless the "vision signal" provided by the Iconoscope. Fortunately, this presents few difficulties. What we do is to send out a radio-frequency carrier wave in just the same manner as we send out a broadcast carrier wave. Then we apply modulation (Chapter III) to this carrier, but instead of the modulation being produced through speech and music, it consists of the amplified current from the Iconoscope—it is, in fact, the "vision signal" itself.

Now we saw when talking of sound broadcasting that the frequency of the carrier wave was much greater than that of the sound waves doing the modulation. Similarly, the carrier waves in television must be of much greater frequency than the vision signals superimposed on them. But these vision signals, on account of the speed at which the beam of electrons scans the mosaic of the iconoscope, are themselves changing very quickly—millions of times per second in fact. Consequently, the carrier wave must be of higher frequency again—50 millions, let us say. This corresponds to a wave-length of six metres, which is about that used for television transmission. One unfortunate result of having to use these very short wave-lengths is that we can only transmit television over a relatively short distance. This is because extremely short waves are not reflected from the ionosphere (see Chapter IV), but go right through it into space. Consequently, the only signals coming to us are those arriving directly along the ground, and on account of the curvature of the earth we cannot receive them at greater distances than we can see—say, about 50 miles, taking into account the height of the transmitting masts. We will improve matters if we build our television stations on high ground, and in fact experiments have been made in which the television signals were retransmitted from an aeroplane circling above the transmitting station, in order to try to increase the area covered by the transmission.

CHAPTER VII

TELEVISION IN INDUSTRY

WHEN TELEVISION is mentioned most people think only of the sets in their own sitting-rooms and of the wonderful way in which their eyes are enabled to penetrate into places that they could never hope to enter in any other way.

They probably remember performances of famous ballerinas, royal occasions, great sporting events in many parts of the world. If they watch their television very often, they will probably feel, quite justly, that they have made almost a personal acquaintance with many great personalities of public life, including politicians, philosophers and scientists.

It would be difficult to exaggerate the benefits to be gained from intelligent use of this marvellous invention. Of no less importance, however, are the vast number of other applications of television about which few ever hear at all. Many of these require far more engineering ingenuity than is ever expended on public broadcasts. I am thinking of the use of TV in factories and laboratories, hospitals and banks, on ships and in aeroplanes, and even below the sea.

In some of these cases television, as the name implies (*tele* is the Greek word for long) simply enables the operator to see objects a long way away and possibly, with the aid of several screens, things that are happening in several distant places at once. In other cases it enables places to be reached that no human being could penetrate because of the difficult, even impossibly dangerous, conditions there.

Two outstanding examples of this are its use by scientists and engineers to examine intensely radioactive interiors of nuclear reactors in the new atomic power stations, and to trace faults in the jet engines of aircraft *while it is in flight*.

Underwater

Another wonderful example of its usefulness was in the search for the submarine *Affray* and, several years afterwards, for the wreckage of the Comet aircraft which crashed for no apparent reason off the island of Elba in the Mediterranean.

Credit for the first really successful use of underwater television goes to the Cornell Aeronautical Laboratory in the United States, which performed five short tests in 1947 that showed how effective it could be. No further use was made of these results, however, and it was not until the *Affray* was lost on a trial underwater cruise four years later that underwater television was put to its first practical test. It came through with flying colours.

The Royal Navy was searching the Channel bottom for the *Affray*, although hope had long since been given up of finding anyone alive inside. The Navy wanted, if it could, to find out *why* the submarine had sunk. The big trouble was that the Channel around the Isle of Wight was littered with hundreds of wrecks. Many of them were so deep or were in areas where currents were so strong and the water so muddy that it was often difficult or impossible to send

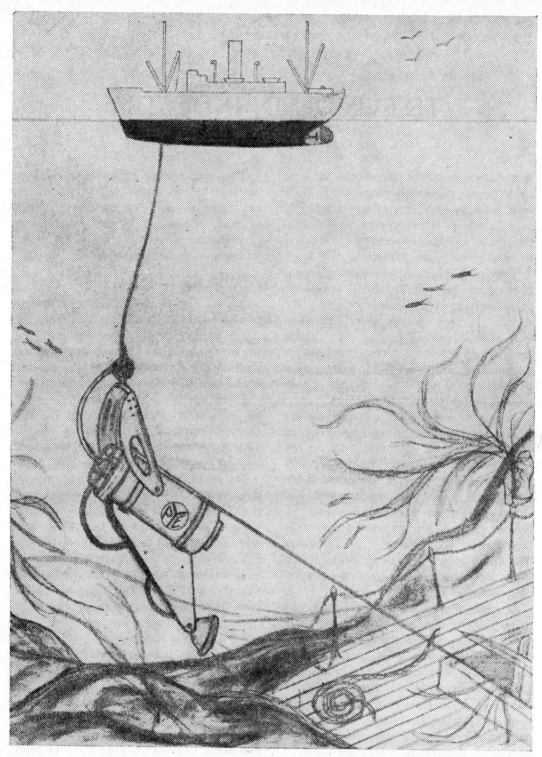

FIGURE 55.   *The camera used to find Comet wreckage in the Mediterranean.*

divers down to see whether a particular wreck, located by their anti-submarine apparatus, was the one they were searching for or not.

The Admiralty was already interested in the idea of underwater television, luckily, and had some time before ordered an ordinary broadcasting type of camera from the Marconi Wireless Telegraph Company. At their request the delivery of this was speeded up.

In the meantime, men of the Royal Naval Scientific Service constructed a waterproof casing for the camera. In three weeks the world's first operational television camera was ready to start the long task of examining one wreck after another until the right one was found.

On June 14, 1951, with the camera operating 258 feet below the surface, two historic "snap-shots" of a television screen in the salvage ship *Reclaim* were taken with a hand-held camera. They were historical because the word AFFRAY, which those on board had already seen, were clearly visible for all the world to see. Later surveys enabled the Navy to find out the cause of the disaster and to make changes of design that would protect future submarines from the same accident.

In Aircraft

In the Britannia aircraft, known as the "Whispering Giant" because of its quiet turbo-propeller engines, television helped to solve a very difficult problem. The engines of this 'plane are among the most powerful in the world. The trouble was that although they behaved perfectly under test on the ground and under most flying conditions, there were some occasions when, for no apparent reason, one of the engines would stop.

When a television camera was fitted into one of the engine nacelles it showed that under certain atmospheric conditions

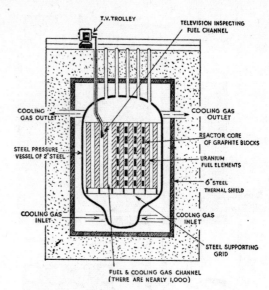

FIGURE 56. *The atomic pile into which the camera is inserted.*

ice at some heights was forming in the air intakes of the engines. At a certain point so much ice would accumulate that chunks of it snapped off and went into the engine, putting out the fuel burners in the all-important combustion chambers. Once engineers knew what was happening it was a fairly easy matter to put the fault right again so that the 'plane could be put into full service.

A Hard Job

The hardest job ever given to makers of industrial television, probably, was when engineers of the Pye Company were asked if they could design and build a television camera that could operate right in the central core of the atomic reactors that provide heat for Calder Hall—the first large-scale nuclear power station in the world. First of all, this meant building a camera that would be small enough to pass down a channel only four and a half inches in diameter. Secondly, it meant designing it in such a way that could stand up to the high temperatures and the

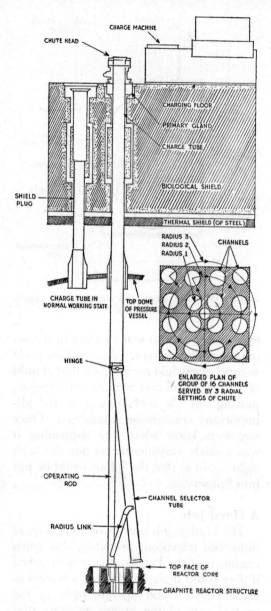

FIGURE 57. *The charge hole fitted with chute ready for recharging.*

devastating radiation that persists in the reactor long after it has been shut down.

To understand better what the camera was required to do we must take a look for a moment at the way the power station is constructed (see Figure 56). The core, you will see, is a honey-comb of graphite blocks which weigh some thousands of tons. This is pierced by 1,596 vertical channels that contain the uranium fuel rods.

It was into these vertical channels that the TV camera was required to pass so that engineers would be able to examine the inside walls from time to time for signs of wear, and also to replace used fuel elements that might be damaged with new ones. This task alone was a pretty hard one, because it had to be operated by remote control from outside the pressure vessel and the successive shields of steel and concrete that enclose the reactor.

To make things more difficult, the Atomic Energy Authority had specified that the camera must be able to stand up to a temperature of 200 degrees Centigrade, equivalent to a medium hot oven, at which many solders melt. They also said that the camera must not contain any metals that might become radioactive themselves after a period within the reactor.

Stiff as the task was, it took only a few months to design and build a camera that met all the requirements. After a preliminary trial in January, 1956, in BEPO, the largest pile operating at Harwell at the time, the new camera was sent up to Calder Hall in Cumberland. Although it was only three and a half inches in diameter and thirty inches long it had a remotely controlled focusing lens and a periscope that could be rotated in any direction. It also had its own built-in floodlight.

To get over the temperature problem, cooling air was supplied to the camera through the control cable to keep the temperature within the camera always below 50 degrees Centigrade. The electric circuits are moulded in a plastic resin called Araldite to give added protection. Any connections not protected in this way were made without the use of solder.

Since then even smaller cameras have been built for Calder Hall to operate in direct conjuction with the remote-controlled fuel grabs. In these, by cutting out of the fittings, such as the periscope and movable focus, from the original model, the measurements were reduced to three inches diameter and twenty inches in length.

While these two cameras for Calder Hall are probably the most spectacular examples of industrial television, there are many other important jobs being done with TV cameras elsewhere. At the Atomic Energy Research Establishment at Harwell, scientists use television to look down microscopes at specimens so radioactive that the rays would reach and destroy human eyes, even through many inches of glass. Another one is used to watch over a machine that can separate out very poisonous substances of only slightly different weights, one atom at a time.

In the Operating Theatre

Any of you who have watched every movement on the face of an actor through "close-ups" on your home television screen will at once realise how useful the TV cameras can be in a hospital, first to give students a far better view of operations than they could ever hope to obtain in a crowded operating theatre, and, secondly, to enable a really large audience of trained surgeons to watch one of their eminent colleagues perform an operation by some new and specially interesting technique. Even better results have been obtained with the use of colour television, because this enables tissue, blood vessels, nerves

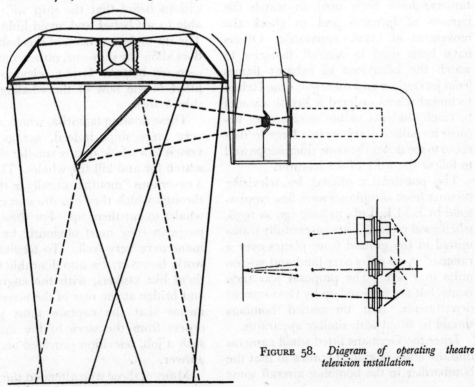

FIGURE 58. *Diagram of operating theatre television installation.*

and muscles to be distinguished more easily.

Two Places at Once

Most of the applications of industrial television that I have described have required specially designed cameras or casings. There are very many others in which a standard industrial type camera—simpler than the type used for broadcasting purposes—can be used just as it is.

In one bank, for example, where the high cost of offices in Central London caused the board to decide to leave the record departments in a country house which they occupied during wartime, television has been used as a link with the head offices, so that a balance sheet or a title deed a score of miles away may be examined almost as easily as if it were ready to hand.

In steel works and power stations cameras have been used to watch the burners of furnaces and to check the movement of heavy apparatus. Others have been used in aircraft factories to watch the behaviour of exhaust flames from jet engines and rockets. One Italian technical school ordered a British camera to teach students to use microscopes because it enabled everyone in a large lecture room to see down the same microscope and to follow the work of the lecturer.

The possibilities offered by televising pictures from aeroplanes were first emphasised by E.M.I., Ltd., as long ago as 1938, when good pictures were successfully transmitted to the ground from planes over a range of 25-50 miles over land and 50-100 miles over sea. The proposal was then made, but not followed up by Government departments, that unmanned bombers should be fitted with similar apparatus.

Later the Germans fitted small cameras into the noses of guided bombs so that the bombardier in the bombing aircraft some distance away could steer the bomb right up to the moment that it hit the target. The American Air Force used a similar method in Korea.

In one of the post-war London radio exhibitions the armed services put on a demonstration of the use of television in a spotter plane to help artillery commanders and to give generals a clear picture of the ground and military operations ahead of them. In a similar way police and the automobile clubs and associations have used television to survey traffic at special meetings and on bank holidays, because it gives controllers a better chance to see what is happening in many different places at once.

One use of television to enable a person to be in two different places at once calls to mind the way in which the Chinese and the Arabs sometimes paint eyes on the bows of their ships because of a superstitious belief that the ship will then be able to see better and avoid hidden reefs. The up-to-date version of this habit really does allow the ship—or, rather, the captain—to see better. It is a television "eye" fitted in the bow of the whaling factory ship *Balena*.

These floating factories, which are often very large ships indeed, act as mother vessels to a whole fleet of smaller ships that search for and kill the whales. They have a cavernous "mouth", usually in the bows, through which they can draw in complete whales to cut them up. For these various purposes they must obviously be able to manœuvre very well. To facilitate their work, however, it is also desirable to shape them like tankers, with the engine-room and bridge at the rear of the vessel, which means that the captain must give his orders from the stern of the ship. For such a job, television provided an obvious answer.

Many of those who attended the notable

meeting of the British Association for the Advancement of Science in Edinburgh in the Duke of Edinburgh's Presidential year will remember for a long time the fine way in which a thousand or more people in an overflow meeting in a neighbouring hall were able to see the Duke give his address on a cinema-size screen with quite remarkable clarity. The faces of those taking part in the opening ceremony were often shown several times life-size in close-ups. The Duke, of course, was well used to the ordeal of being under continuous observation, but the audience, which included many students, had great fun in watching in such detail the faces of the other unsuspecting personalities on the stage, including some of their own professors, as they yawned freely during some of the more lengthy and less interesting portions of the opening ceremony and smiled freely or frowned on other occasions.

An enterprising motor firm in the United States put television to quite a different use recently when it wanted to tell its sales representatives all over the country about a new model it was bringing out. It had the idea of televising a demonstration and lecture to centres in every state instead of spending many hundreds of thousands of dollars on bringing them to Detroit and putting them up for the night in expensive hotels.

The same technique can save the time of highly paid staff men by avoiding much shorter journeys than that. A well-known London watch company uses it to enable engineers in various parts of a very extensive factory to consult their chief when in difficulty. Instead of calling him over, if their work is not transportable, all they have to do is to show him their problem with the aid of a portable television camera in one of several laboratories and machine shops.

One recent example of another kind will show just how unlimited the flexibility of this new twentieth-century tool is. It comes from the Institute of Aviation Medicine at Farnborough, Hants, where doctors and scientists carry out research on problems of high-speed flight. The camera in this case is in a cabin at the end of a 60-foot long rotating arm that simulates the conditions that a pilot of a supersonic aircraft suffers when he suddenly changes direction. The purpose of the camera, in this case, of course, was to allow the doctors in charge of the experiment to see just what happened to the pilot and to make sure that he did not come to any harm.

The many uses of television that I have just described represent only a small fraction of the total that have *already* been put into practice or investigated. The full list would be almost endless, and it must be remembered that television is still in its infancy. It was only as recently as November, 1936, that the world's first regular television programme was first radiated from London. Not even the most fertile brain could imagine all the uses that will be found for it in the future.

CHAPTER VIII

ACHIEVING THE IMPOSSIBLE

THE SHADOWS of war had been hanging over Europe long before 1939, and far-seeing people in England had no illusions about whether or not this country would ultimately be involved. They knew, above all, that any future war would be far different from any that had been waged before—it would be predominantly an *air* war, a bombers' war, with the whole civilian population of these islands exposed to attack just as much as men in the front line, if there was, indeed, any "front line" at all.

They cast about, therefore, for means to defend us from this threat, and it is to their lasting credit that they did this long before the attack ultimately came, with the result that to a great extent we were ready for it. We won the Battle of Britain through the skill of our pilots and the excellence of our machines; but how many know enough of what had really gone on behind the scenes to understand that the finest pilots and machines in the world might not have availed without the assistance of the electron and the marvellous electron-driven devices which gave us warning of the enemy's approach long before he could be seen and heard, which told us how many bombers were approaching, and could even distinguish between friend and foe.

For this was the next task, after he had successfully given us television, that man asked the electron to accomplish. And what a task! To understand exactly *what* we were asking, consider the difference between the problems facing the television engineer and those facing the men responsible for what has now commonly become known as radar, a manufactured word descriptive of the phrase, "Radio Direction-finding and Ranging".

Essentially the problem facing these two sets of men is the same. Both are concerned with "seeing things out of sight". To accomplish television, however, the engineer has an image-recording and transmitting device actually on the spot, and his only concern is to send an image in the form of radio waves to a conveniently situated receiver which incorporates the necessary devices for turning the radio waves back into a visual image.

Things are very different for the radar engineer, however. He, too, has to see something out of sight—an aeroplane, a ship or a submarine—but not only has he no apparatus on the actual object he wishes to see, but he has to *see* it, find out its *distance* from him, find out its *bearing*, and, in the case of an aeroplane, its *flying height*. In a word, he has to fix the exact position in space of an object which he cannot see and with which he can have no connection except that mysterious something which we call the "ether".

My task in this chapter is to explain to you simply and clearly the *principles* on which various radar devices worked. These principles are not beyond the comprehension of any boy who knows the elementary facts of electricity and magnetism, and who has read carefully what has previously been written about radio waves and the cathode ray tube. As a matter of fact, the solution of the many problems confronting the radar engineer was only possible because of the work that had previously been done in radio and television, and between the technique of the latter and radar there is a very strong link.

In the end, however, it is due to the fact that in this country and America men had directed their energies, not so much towards the provision of bigger and better radio sets, but towards finding out the things that happened to radio waves when they travelled about the world, and the nature of the interfering waves which prevented the fullest use of the waves carrying communications, that radar and all its developments came into being.

The main job to which British military scientists were addressing themselves in 1935 and 1936 was essentially the *location in space* of a hostile aeroplane approaching our coasts.

Now it is perfectly easy to find the height of anything we can see clearly, but the radar problem was quite different. In the first place, the target *moved* continuously, and in the second place in most cases it could not be *seen*, by reason of cloud, fog, darkness or sheer distance away. Yet it was still necessary to know *three things* about it.

(1) Its actual *direct* distance away, i.e. what is called its "slant range".

(2) Its "compass bearing" or direction from the magnetic north.

(3) Its actual height above the ground.

The drawing in Figure 59 shows how knowing these three dimensions enables one to calculate exactly where the target is situated in space relative to the observer so that guns can be brought to bear on it or aeroplanes sent to meet it.

Let us first consider the actual direct distance away of the object it is desired to locate. How would you tackle the solution of such a problem?

In the first place, have we anything to go on? Yes, I think we have. Suppose you stand a considerable distance away

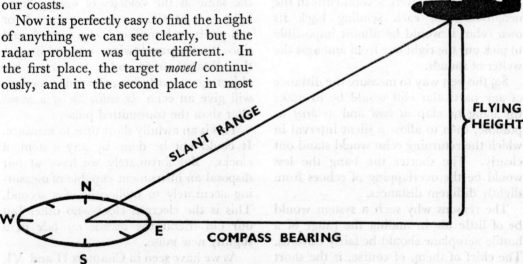

FLYING HEIGHT

SLANT RANGE

COMPASS BEARING

N
W   E
S

FIGURE 59. *Finding the actual position of an aeroplane in space needs a knowledge of three things;*
(1) *its slant range, or the distance it happens to be from any particular spot chosen on the ground;*
(2) *its flying height, which is its height above sea-level or any other level chosen as the datum line;*
and (3) *its compass bearing or bearing from the magnetic north.*
The electron echo system known as "radar" made it possible to get all these measurements automatically on one instrument, no matter how fast the plane was travelling.

from a tall cliff. How could you find how far away the cliff was? I think you would immediately jump to the idea of using an *echo*.

The Speed of Sound

The procedure would be to make a sharp handclap, or give a short, sharp shout. Then, if the exact time it took for the shout to come back as an echo was measured, the distance away of the cliff could easily be calculated. We know that it takes ten seconds for sound to travel a mile and back, so that we can change sound-seconds into miles. If the echo came back thirty seconds after the handclap the cliff must have been three miles away.

Now the louder the clap, the louder the echo and the further back from the cliff we could go and still hear the echo clearly. However, if the clapping were continuous the loud, local noise might cover up the echo and the latter would not be heard. Similarly, if there were several cliffs in the neighbourhood, each sending back its own echo, it would be almost impossible to pick out the right one from amongst the welter of sounds.

So, the best way to measure the distance of any particular cliff would be to make the bang or clap *as loud* and *as brief* as possible, then to allow a silent interval in which the returning echo would stand out clearly. The shorter the bang the less would be the overlapping of echoes from slightly different distances.

The reasons why such a system would be of little use in finding the range of a hostile aeroplane should be fairly obvious. The chief of them, of course, is the short range of sound. But very fortunately we have a *radio equivalent* of a handclap. This is called a radio "pulse" and consists of a series of very short trains of radio waves sent out from a transmitting station,

between each "pulse" occurring an interval during which nothing happens (Figure 60).

Now the fact that radio waves have optical properties—such properties as reflection possessed by ordinary light—was shown as long ago as 1886 in the famous experiments of Heinrich Hertz, the discoverer of radio waves. Hertz showed, amongst other things, that radio waves were reflected from solid objects. If, therefore, we sent out a very strong one of these pulses we should rightly expect that a suitable detecting device would be able to register the "echo" when it arrived, and from the time-interval between the sending out of the pulse and the reception of the echo we should be able to calculate the distance of the object reflecting the wave in the same way as we calculated the distance of the cliff. That is, provided we know the rate at which radio waves travel.

We do, of course, know this rate. It is the same as the velocity of light. Since light goes at 186,000 miles a second, or 328 yards each millionth of a second, and since it must travel twice—out and back—the distance from radar to target, an object 1,000 yards from the radar receiver will give an echo *six millionths of a second* later than the transmitted pulse.

This is an awfully short time to measure. It could not be done by any system of clocks. But fortunately we have at our disposal an instrument capable of measuring accurately to millionths of a second. This is the electron clock—no other but our old friend the *cathode ray tube* in a slightly new guise.

As we have seen in Chapters II and VI, the cathode ray tube depends for its usefulness in this sphere on the facts that a fine pencil of electrons produces a bright spot on the fluorescent screen at the end of the tube, and that deflection of the

(Top) *Television lighting control position in apparatus room, for the resistance dimming equipment used in the studio. The monitor screens of the camera control unit console are just visible above the central desk.*

(Right) *Electro-magnetic clutch assemblies in the dimmer room of a television studio.*

(Above) *Side view of a three-tube colour camera, showing one of the camera tubes in its yoke and its associated amplifiers.* (Right) *Experimental colour camera.* (Below) *Control room of the BBC experimental colour studio, showing sound desk on the left, vision mixing desk in centre and two camera control positions on the right. At the far wall are the three coders, together with measuring equipment.*

General view of television studio floor with producer's control room across corner (at the top of picture).

The television control gallery overlooking the studio with the producer, his secretary, assistant producer and vision mixer on far side.

Television cameras in action.

Industrial type vidicon camera mounted for periscope shots in control room of a submarine for outside broadcast.

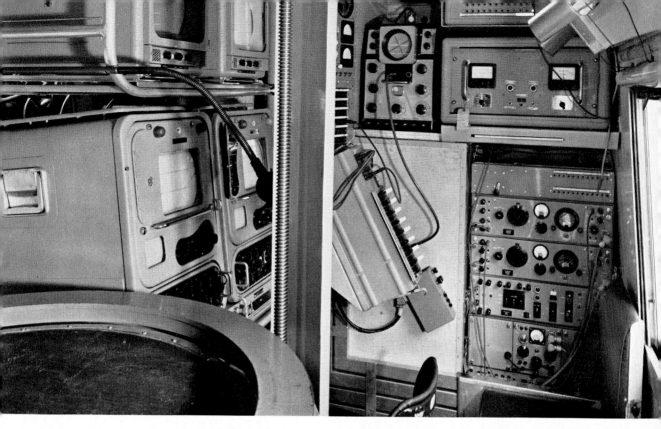

BBC television roving eye van equipment: Camera control monitors and radio check monitors on the left; sound communication equipment on the right. Left foreground, camera lift; centre top, aerial bearing dial.

BBC camera mounted on top of cairn at the very summit of Snowdon, 3,560 ft.

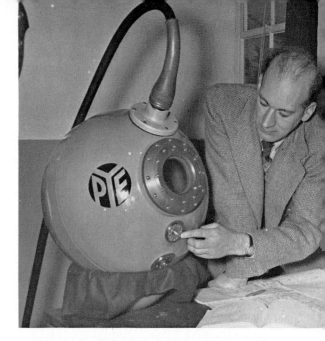

Hand-held camera operated by a frogman. The cylindrical object on the top is an underwater loudspeaker. The square frames are for aiming the camera. The instrument has four lenses that can be changed by remote control.

The same camera in a spherical case can operate down to depths of 3,000 ft. below the surface. The diaphragm being indicated is to measure depth.

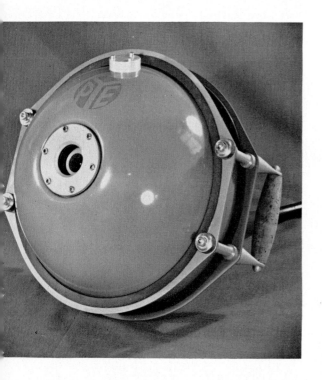

(Above) A miniature underwater television camera only 1 ft. in diameter, intended for use by frogmen. The electronic apparatus in this device is of standard industrial type, extremely simple in form. The camera is intended for normal use down to a depth of 200 ft. (Right) Monitoring set and control cabinet for the underwater television apparatus.

electron beam by electric or magnetic forces can make the spot move. It can be made to move from right to left, for example, in any desired time, and it can be made to stay "off right" for any desired period, after which it can be caused to jump back almost simultaneously to its former left-hand position, and repeat the process at any regular rate required. The method by which all this can be done was fully described in the chapter on television, and we need go no further into it here.

However, as we have seen previously, another set of electric or magnetic forces can make the spot move vertically, up or down, and if these forces are governed by a radio receiver into which the "echo" pulses are fed from a receiving aerial, each pulse will make a V-shaped notch in the horizontal line. If, moreover, this process is being repeated many times a second, "persistence of vision" will cause us to see a bright line, complete with notch, drawn continuously on the cathode ray tube.

How the Echo is made Visible

We have now all the essentials for setting up our first ground radar system for "early warning of approaching aircraft".

First we set up a transmitting set which is able to send out very powerful pulses at exactly equal intervals—say, every one-twenty-fifth of a second for long distances, or even one-five-thousandth of a second for short distances. This means that for

about a millionth of a second (a microsecond, written μ sec.) the transmitter is radiating a power of several hundred thousands of watts, and then is absolutely dead for about 40,000 microseconds, after which it again is active for a microsecond, and so on. Figure 61 should make the arithmetic of this quite plain.

These pulses are sent out by a big transmitting aerial so arranged that they spread out nearly uniformly over a wide area in front of the station, but spread very little behind. This is to avoid confusion from our own aircraft, which may be operating inland.

A hundred yards or so away we put up a receiving aerial and let it feed the radio receiver connected with our cathode ray tube. Every time a pulse starts out from the transmitter we cause the spot on the screen of the tube to start its travel from left to right, and the big "bang" in the receiver due to the wave from a hundred yards away makes a big notch, called by the radar operators a "blip", at the left-hand starting end of the line. Now we arrange for the line to re-draw itself at exactly the same speed as the pulses are going out, so that the blips due to successive pulses all occur in exactly the same place—they are superimposed—and the impression of a stationary blip is given.

Suppose that an echo pulse comes back from an aircraft. We know that it will arrive ten microseconds later than the transmitted pulse for every mile the

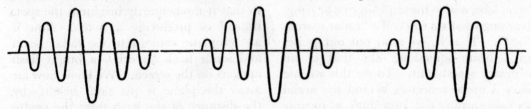

FIGURE 60. *Radio pulse in diagram form. A radio pulse is a series of very short trains of waves with intervals between them during which the transmitter is silent. The purpose of the pulse is to send a short wave out into space which can return as an echo, and a continuous tone would cause the returning echo to be muddled. This is the fundamental principle of radar—to send out a pulse and judge the distance to the object by the time taken for the echo to return.*

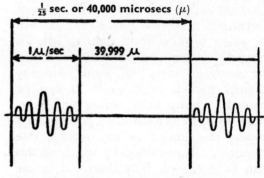

FIGURE 61. *A radio echo is so rapid that it could not possibly be measured by any ordinary means. Fortunately, however, this very short interval of time can be measured by the electron beam of the cathode ray tube or oscilloscope, and what happens in practice is that a notch appears in the fluorescent line on the screen and shows the actual distance of the object which reflected the pulse.*

aircraft is distant; moreover, it will itself make a blip or notch in the horizontal line, and this notch will occur at a point along the line reached by the spot after it has been travelling that number of microseconds. An aircraft echo therefore makes a slowly moving notch, the left-hand edge of which reads the distance of the aircraft on the horizontal scale which we graduate in miles by putting a one-mile-graduation for every ten microseconds left to right travel of the spot. This may seem a little difficult to understand, but it is hoped that Figure 62 will make the idea plain.

In the foregoing, we sketched a system for finding the direct distance of an aeroplane from the radar station. We still have to find its compass bearing and its flying height before we can fix the exact position of the aircraft in space.

Finding the Compass Bearing by Radar

We can determine the slant range of an aeroplane, and at the same time its bearing, by using what we will call a "radar searchlight". That is, we send out our pulses in a beam something like that of an ordinary searchlight. To do this we use curved metal reflectors behind the aerial to concentrate the rays into a narrow beam, just as the curved mirror in a searchlight does for the light rays. The next step is to rotate the aerial and re-

flector steadily round, so that pulses are sent out in every direction in turn. Our radar searchlight has become a radar lighthouse, rotating about ten times a minute. Now let us look at the receiving end. First of all our receiving aerial with its reflector is rotated in step with the transmitting aerial, so as always to be in a position to pick up reflected pulses. The cathode ray tube on which the signals are displayed is operated in rather a different manner from before. First of all we start the spot off from the centre of the screen instead of from the left-hand edge, but just as before it moves over to the edge of the screen, and then returns extremely rapidly to the centre again, thus drawing the line on which the blips will appear. But besides this we cause the whole line to rotate steadily round the tube like the spoke of a wheel, exactly in step with the aerials moving round outside. We have used up both pairs of deflecting plates in doing this, and so we apply the incoming signal to the modulator grid of the tube, so that it momentarily brightens the spot, instead of producing a notch. Now if an aeroplane comes into the radar beam and sends back an echo, a bright flash appears on the screen. We know how far away the plane is (its slant height) by the distance of the flash from the centre of the screen, just as before, while we know in what direction it is (its bearing) by noting how far round our line has rotated. We generally keep the normal brightness of the spot so low as to be almost invisible, so that all we see on the screen is the flash indicating the position of the plane. Now it would be much more convenient if, instead of just getting a flash on the screen every six seconds or so, when our "radar lighthouse" illuminates the plane, we could get a steady dot. We can do this if we employ a special coating on the end of our cathode ray tube, which will continue to glow between the time one flash occurs and the next one comes along. We thus get a practically steady dot on the screen.

If there are two or more planes approaching the radar station we get the corresponding number of dots, indicating the position and bearing of each of them. Nor are we limited just to looking at aeroplanes. The photographs on page 124 show how we can get quite an accu-rate "map" of the Thames adjacent to Hammersmith Bridge. You will see at once how immensely helpful this can be, especially at night or in fog, as radar can "see" just as well then as in broad day-light. This ingenious system we have been discussing is known as PPI, these letters standing for Plan Position Indicator.

Measuring height by Radio Reflection

Remembering what was said about radio waves having some properties similar to those of light waves, Figure 63 shows clearly that the echo pulse travelling from the aircraft reaches an elevated aerial by two routes, one direct and another after reflection from the ground. This is be-cause, generally, the ground acts as a nearly perfect "radio mirror".

However, in the process of reflection an unexpected thing takes place. If the *peak* of an incident wave hits the ground,

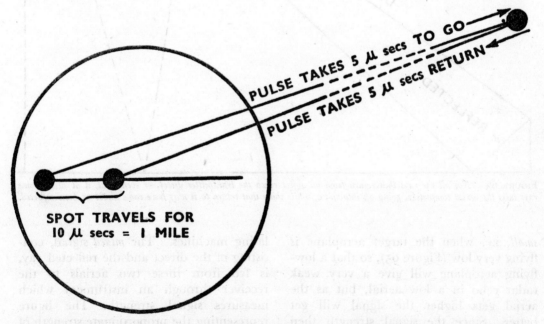

FIGURE 62. *When the radio pulse is sent out, the spot on the screen is at the left side, and it travels across it for a certain length of time representing so many miles. Anything that returns during that time causes the spot to waver, and the constant repetition of pulse and echo makes a continuous picture of the distance of the wavering "notch" from the beginning of the pulse.*

the reflected wave does not start off from the ground as a peak, but as a *trough*; vice versa, if it is the trough of the incident ray which meets the ground, the reflected ray leaves the ground as a peak. What this means in the receiver is not hard to understand.

If, at any instant of time, the peak of a wave in the *direct* ray is entering the receiver, it will be the *trough* of the reflected ray that is entering—in other words, the two signals will *cancel one another out* (Figure 64).

Now this effect is most noticeable when the angles made by the incident and reflected rays with the ground are very

merely by comparing the signals from the two.

It would take several minutes to make the calculation, but at a radar station it is all done automatically by special calcu-

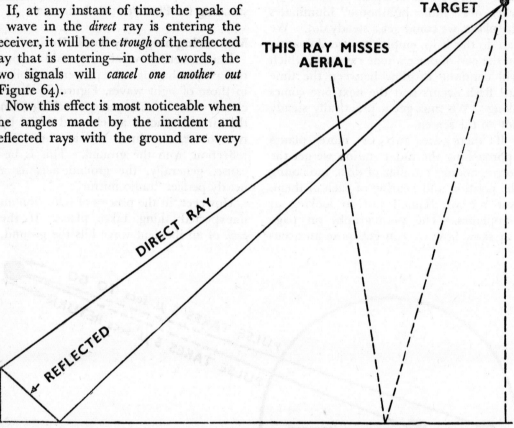

TARGET

THIS RAY MISSES AERIAL

DIRECT RAY

REFLECTED

FIGURE 63. *Not all the rays that return from an object reach the transmitter direct, or even reach it at all. Some rays miss the aerial completely, going off into space, while those that return to it may have come direct or been reflected.*

small, i.e. when the target aeroplane is flying very low (Figure 65), so that a low-flying aeroplane will give a very weak radar echo in a low aerial, but as the aerial gets higher the signal will get better. Since the signal strength then depends on the height of the aerial, by using two aerials of different heights we can calculate the altitude of the plane,

lating machines. The *mixed* signal, consisting of the direct and the reflected ray, is fed from these two aerials to the receiver through an instrument which measures signal strength. The figure representing the proportionate strength of the two signals is then sent to the plotting room, and in an instant the flying height of the target aeroplane becomes known.

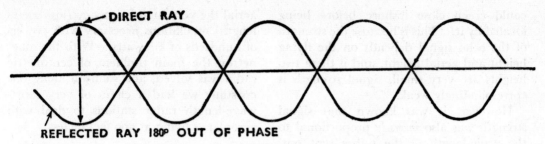

FIGURE 64. *Diagram showing that the reflected ray from an object causing an electron "echo" is exactly opposite in period (time it reaches its highest value) to the direct ray.*

You can see that we should also be able to determine elevation with a radar "searchlight". In this case we would need a beam confined to a narrow horizontal plane—a lighthouse on its side, so to speak—and this method has in fact been successfully used in practice.

Such was the radar system developed from the experiments of far-seeing men in the late spring of 1935 on a small island off the East Coast. Work began in 1936 toward setting up a British Home Chain of five stations for giving early warning, and this was completed in the autumn of that year. By March 1938 all these stations—the nucleus of a great final chain which "floodlit" the whole of Britain's coastline—were in operation.

After this, development work on radar never stood still, and a whole series of new devices were gradually brought into being which vastly extended its scope. Nowadays radar refers to no single instrument.

An individual radar set may be a hundred-pound outfit, the size and shape of a small bomb, for installation in a fast aeroplane; or it may be a sprawling complex of shacks and trucks with its own telephone exchange, with a giant antenna structure, and with a whole company of soldiers to man it. It may be five tons of equipment in a large aircraft carrier, or it may be a couple of water-tight boxes on deck and a modest bulge on the mast of a motor launch. Some of the latest sets, intended for guided weapons, weigh only a few pounds.

But despite the difference in the forms of radar used, there is a common set of principles behind their operation. These principles we have described. The sort of development that took place is most aptly illustrated by the introduction of "centimetric radio".

The great problem with the early radar installations was that low-flying aircraft

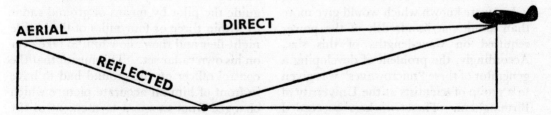

FIGURE 65. *A plane can fly too low to be caught by the radar sounding apparatus. It is too low when the angle made by the two rays that return from it, the direct and the reflected rays, make too sharp an angle.*

could creep close inshore before being located by it. This is because the strength of the echo signal depends on the flying height and aerial height, and if these two heights are very small, signal strength is correspondingly weak.

However, it was known that signal strength was also *inversely* proportional to the wave-length of the pulses sent out. The smaller the wave-length of these pulses, that is, the stronger the signal. Now the wave-lengths that had been used were already very small compared to, say, the wave-lengths used for broadcasting. Whereas the latter used an average of 400 metres, the early radar worked on a metre and a half.

Clearly, what was wanted was a wave-length of a few centimetres. This would solve the problem of detecting the low-flying plane, and it had the great advantage that these short waves could be concentrated much more easily into our radar "searchlight" beam. Something of a disadvantage, on the other hand, was that such short-wave beams, unlike those composed of longer wave-lengths, do not follow the curvature of the earth. Radar sets using them could not see *over* the optical horizon, although they could see a plane out *at* the optical horizon, which may in the case of a high-flying plane amount to a hundred miles. We met the same problem even with the somewhat longer wave-lengths used in television.

At the time, however, no transmitting valves were known which would give more than about one-hundredth of the power required on wave-lengths of this size. Accordingly, the problem of developing a generator of these "microwaves" was given to a group of scientists at the University of Birmingham. These workers succeeded in developing a new type of valve, called a "magnetron", which generated in the

aerial the very high-frequency (low-wave-length) oscillations necessary with powers of hundreds of kilowatts. With the magnetron the main problem of centimetric radio was solved, and soon all along our coastline we had a chain of very short-wave-length radar stations to deal with aeroplanes flying at 500 feet or less.

Distinguishing one Plane from another

The next problem that cropped up concerned distinguishing friend from foe in this game of aerial identification. Blips might be due to enemy planes, or they might result from our own planes in search of them. This problem was solved when we were able to fit in our planes a small set which would not only receive the radar pulses, but would send back a magnified and easily recognisable version of them, thus saying, "I am a friend", or, as it became possible to *code* the message sent through the friendly blip, the airman could say, "I am a particular sort of friend".

Radar Sets for Fighter Planes

Night fighting, too, was immeasurably assisted by radar when it was possible to manufacture a radar sending and receiving set small enough to be carried in a fighter plane. The range of this set, however, was only some two and a half to four miles and unless the pilot was within this distance of his target he had little hope of finding it. The job, therefore, was to guide the pilot by means of ground radar to within three or four miles of the hostile night-flier and then allow him to take over on his own radar set. This meant that the control officer on the ground had to have in front of him an accurate picture which changed from moment to moment of the disposition of all the aeroplanes in the sky at any particular time; in addition he had

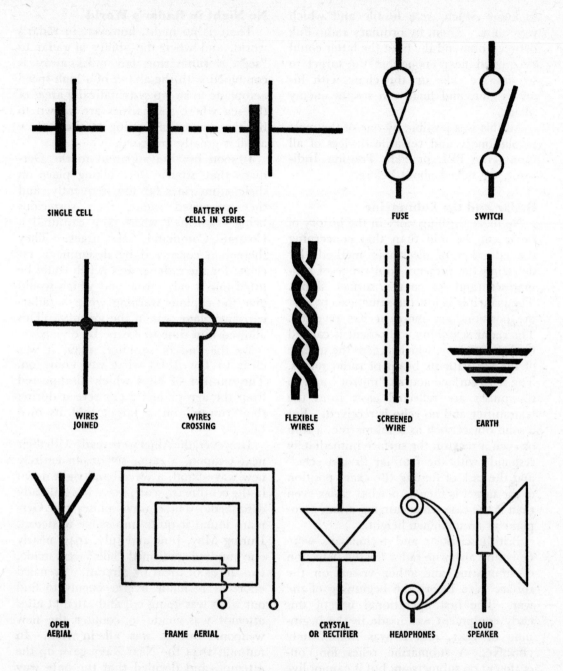

FIGURE 66a. *Standard symbols set out by the British Standards Institution to simplify the interpretation of diagrams.*

to know which were hostile and which were ours. Then, by ordinary radio link between him and the pilot the latter could be guided near enough to the target to be able to take up the chase with his own radar, and finally to see the enemy plane.

All this was possible by one of the most revolutionary and versatile devices of all radar—the PPI, or Plan Position Indicator, we talked about before.

Radar and the Submarine

No more thrilling story in the history of radar can be told than that concerning the adoption of electronic methods for detecting the presence and range of submarines (and, of course, surface ships). The principle is just the same, except that the positions are more or less reversed. The radar searching equipment is carried by the aeroplane, which sweeps the surface of the sea with its beam of radio pulses. The sea's surface acts as "mirror" and so the pulses are reflected *away* from the transmitter and no echo is received. But a solid object such as a submarine, a ship or even a rock on the surface immediately responds with the familiar "radio echo" and the task of finding the exact position of the target is then somewhat easier even than is the case when ranging on an aeroplane at an unknown height.

British scientists and technicians were designing airborne radar for the detection of submarine and other vessels on the surface even before the beginning of the war. The first operational use of this early equipment was made in the beginning of 1941, and it was immediately effective. A submarine relies for concealment on submersion, but it cannot live indefinitely under water. It must come to the surface to charge its batteries and take in fresh air, and usually it did this by night.

No Night in Radar's World

There is no night, however, in radar's world, and when the ability of radar to "see" a submarine ten miles away is combined with the ability of a high-speed aeroplane to sweep systematically areas of the sea where submarines are known to be, the danger of coming to the surface at all is greatly increased.

It soon became apparent to the Germans that attacks were taking place on their submarines far too frequently, and they suspected radar, their suspicions being confirmed when they captured a Coastal Command set intact. They thereupon countered by designing a receiver for the radar pulses which could be fitted into a submarine and which would give the captain warning when a radar-carrying plane was in the vicinity. This allowed him time to escape by diving.

By the end of summer, 1942, it was clear to the Allies what was going on. The number of blips which disappeared from the aeroplane's radar screen during the "run-in" on a target told its own tale.

However, the Allies were ready with their next weapon, a radar set on an entirely new wave-band, a wave-band right down in the centimetre scale, as we have already described. These wave pulses the Germans found it quite impossible to detect. During May, June and July, 1943, nearly one hundred confirmed "kills" were made, two-thirds of them by aircraft. Frenzied efforts were made by the enemy to find out what was going on, and attempt after attempt was made to counter the new weapon. But it was all in vain. In autumn 1944 the Nazi Navy gave up the attempt, and decided that the only way for a submarine to live was not to come up at all. They were busy installing an air-tube they called schnorkel, which enabled a U-boat to breathe and run its

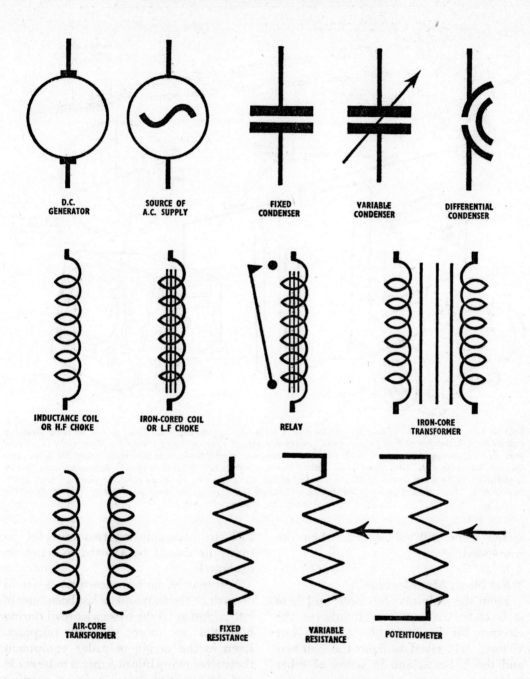

FIGURE 66b. *More symbols in general use among designers of radio apparatus.*

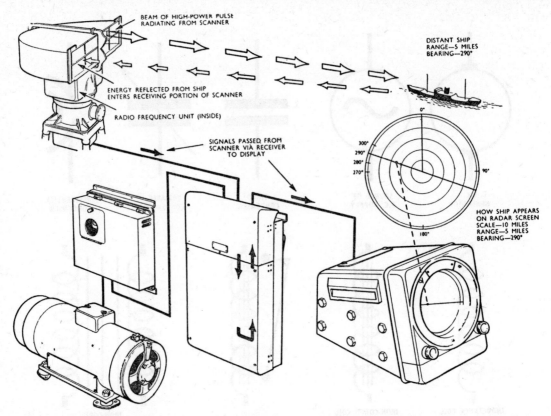

FIGURE 67. *Plotting a naval position with the help of radar: the transmitter, which forms part of the radio frequency unit produces short pulses of high frequency radio energy at a rate of 1,000 or 500 per second. This energy is radiated from the upper portion of the scanner in the form of a narrow, concentrated beam. As the scanner rotates the beam scans the area around the ship. Any object in the path of the beam reflects back a small amount of transmitted energy; this is picked up by the lower portion of the scanner and passed, via a receiving section in the radio frequency unit, to the receiver unit. From there it passes to the display unit, where it appears on the screen as a spot of light at the correct range and bearing.*

diesels while still submerged, when the war ended.

What Now, Mr. Electron?

From the little that has been said here it is clear that we owe thanks to the electron for the share he took in our victory. He saved us from the bombers and the U-boats, and in scores of other ways too numerous to mention in this short chapter he enabled us to create devices which enabled us to do what in other wars was deemed impossible. In radar, and especially in the wonderful

PPI, he accomplished two miracles, so surely he should be allowed to retire on his laurels.

Fortunately, he has shown no desire to do so since the war, and he has been busy of late adapting all the lessons learned during hostilities to more peaceful purposes. Even in the design of radar equipment there were many improvements to be made and the scientists show no sign of running out of ideas. One of the first developments, and one that has proved to be of very great importance, is the use of what is known as the "Doppler Principle" to cut out stationary objects from a radar screen, or vice versa. Thus, the controllers at airports are able to see fast-moving aeroplanes in the area without being troubled by confusing reflections from clouds and local landmarks.

Another development of tremendous importance to navigators is a type of radar that shows the ship on which the set is carried as a moving object, proceeding in its true direction and correct speed, instead of as a stationary object at the centre of the screen. Other developments have not all been so spectacular as radar, but they will have a beneficial influence on all our lives. Some of them are dealt with in later chapters.

CHAPTER IX

BLIND NAVIGATION

ONE OF the most important things the electron has done in man's service is to make safer his travels about the surface of the earth, both by sea and in the air. Most of the perils that faced the mariner, for instance, arose from the fact that he either did not know or had erroneous notions about where he was. Storms could put him off his course; fogs could blind him. His compass, even, could lead him astray.

For properly equipped ships, those dangers had been largely eliminated before the last war, and it was legally necessary for all ships above a certain size to carry approved direction-finding apparatus. The development of radar during the war, however, has vastly improved matters, and although the future will see most big ships fitted with some form of radar position-finding apparatus, the older equipment is not out of date by any means, and is even likely to be improved by what we have learned.

The whole principle of direction-finding by wireless can be illustrated by an experiment you can make for yourself if you possess a portable wireless with a "frame aerial" or are energetic and enterprising enough to fit one to your home wireless receiver.

The frame aerial consists of a number of turns of wire arranged to form a "loop" (Figure 68). The most important property of a frame aerial is that it picks up the loudest signal from a transmitting station when it is turned *parallel* to the direction from which the transmitted signals are coming; the strength of the received signal is *least* when the plane of the aerial is broadside on to the incoming waves. The figure tries to show this graphically.

Tune your portable, therefore, to a known station some distance away. Then gradually turn the set on a vertical axis until you find the position where the signals appear to be loudest. Mark the position. Now slowly rotate the set until the signal is either not heard at all or is very weak. The position in which this occurs should be marked, and it will generally be found that it is fixed at a point where the set has been turned through a right angle.

But if you practise carefully, you will find that it is easiest to determine when the sound is weakest. Obviously, it is strongest when the set is *end on* to the station, but it is better to say that the direction of the station is indicated by a line drawn at right angles to the set when the signal is weakest.

This is the method most usually employed in practice, although it is not necessary to have the actual aerial a rotating one. A rotating aerial, particularly if it is at all large, can be a nuisance in practice, and engineers therefore devised a method whereby they could obtain the effect of a rotating aerial although the frames were in fact fixed in position.

The problem was solved by using two separate fixed aerials, one of which was placed in a North-South plane, the other

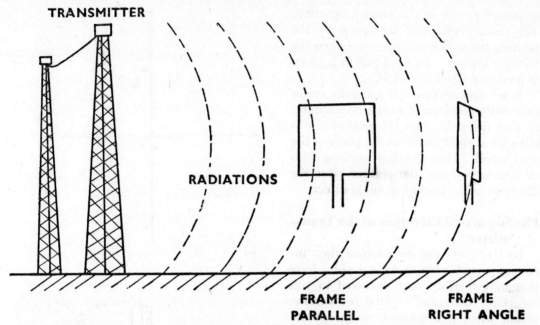

FIGURE 68. *A rotating frame aerial will pick up signals of varying strength according to the angle it makes with the direction in which the waves are travelling. When it is parallel or end-on to them the signals are loudest, and when it is at right angles the signals are weakest.*

in an East-West plane. The two aerials are usually in the form of loops with the same vertical axis, one loop being inside the other and at right angles to it.

How the Radio-goniometer Works

Leads, two from each loop, are then taken to an instrument called a radio-goniometer, or wireless angle-measurer. The two leads from the North-South loop are connected to a fixed coil in the radio-goniometer. The two leads from the East-West loop are connected to a second coil set at right angles to the first. These two coils have the same vertical axis, and inside them (Figure 69) is a search coil which can be rotated at will round the same vertical axis. To the top of the spindle carrying the search coil a pointer is fixed, and this pointer moves round a horizontal dial graduated clockwise in 360 degrees, starting with zero at the

North. East is 90 degrees, West is 270 degrees and South 180 degrees.

When the search coil of the goniometer is rotated the effect is exactly the same as when a frame aerial is rotated. A signal coming from the North or South is picked up by the North-South loop. The search coil, then, gives maximum signal when it is in the plane of the North-South fixed coil of the goniometer. Similarly, a signal from East or West only affects the East-West aerial loop and the search coil gives maximum signal when in the plane of the East-West fixed coil of the goniometer.

Usually, however, the signal will come in at an angle between the two loops. Say it comes in at the angle shown in Figure 69. Such a signal will distribute itself in a certain proportion between the two aerial loops, and the effect of the signal will therefore be conveyed to the two goniometer coils in the same proportion. The *resultant effect* will be shown by the position the search coil takes up when the signal is loudest. In the figure it is given as 30 degrees East of North.

As we said earlier, it is generally easier to identify positions of minimum strength, so that the pointer of the goniometer is often set at right angles to the plane of the search coil. Hence, when working with minimum positions the pointer gives the direction of the incoming signal direct.

Finding actual Direction of the Transmitter

We say gives the direction of the "incoming signal", but there is a point here that may possibly have occurred to you regarding "direction". All that the frame aerial, when it is rotated, or the goniometer can do on its own is to give the direction of the "line" along which the waves from any particular transmitter are reaching the receiver.

That is to say, if a rotated aerial gives this line as running from North to South, we are still unable to say, save from previous knowledge, whether the transmitter itself is North or South of us. All that the frame aerial indicates is that it is on the North-South line passing through our own position, on one side or the other.

Otherwise expressed, if we get, say, a maximum with our frame aerial or goniometer coil in a certain position, then we will also get a maximum when we turn it through 180 degrees. To make certain from which side the waves are coming it is necessary to use an additional aerial— a simple vertical one, which, of course, responds equally well to signals from all directions. For simplicity we will just consider how this can be done with a rotating frame aerial, but the radiogoniometer works in exactly the same way. With our frame aerial adjusted for maxi-

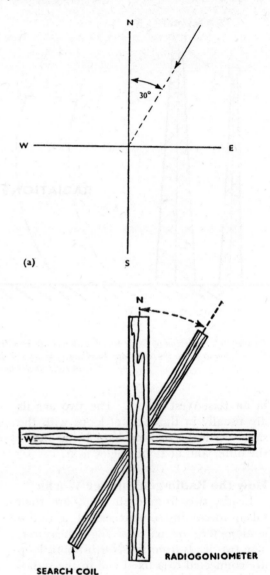

FIGURE 69. *Instead of a rotating aerial, it is possible to use two fixed frame aerials set at right angles to each other, with a rotating coil to pick up the direction from which the waves are coming. Three coils are used in all, two fixed coils, which are set at right angles like the two frame aerials above, and a search coil, set between them so that it rotates on the same axis.*

mum current, we can arrange for the signals from the vertical to help it and thus double the current. Now when we turn our frame aerial through 180 degrees, the current produced in it will be out of phase with that from the vertical aerial and will cancel out, giving us no sound at all in our headphones. We thus know in which of the two directions the transmitting station really is. The vertical aerial we have been talking about above is known as a "sense-finder".

The procedure we have described applies to direction-finding from a fixed station on land, since the aerial loops are fixed in North-South and East-West positions. On board ship this is not possible, as they would have to be continually adjusted to point in the correct direction. So one of the loops on board ship is fixed with its plane fore and aft, the other at right angles to it. We know from the compass the direction in which the ship is steaming, and combining this with the goniometer reading gives us the bearing of the transmitting station. However, this is generally done automatically by a special gyro device, which gives the answer straight away.

Let us now see how direction-finding by wireless can be used in navigating a ship, using our own portable wireless first.

Suppose your room is the wireless cabin of a ship which is sailing on a certain compass course through a thick fog. You require to know your exact position.

How to Experiment at Home

Obviously, we cannot have the use of a complicated arrangement like a sense-finder, so we shall have to assume that we already know roughly our direction from the transmitting station. As a matter of fact, in the actual navigation of a ship, this is a fact that is nearly always known, because the navigator is not "dumped" unexpectedly in some unknown sea and expected to find his position there, but

travels usually from one known spot to another, keeping a careful record of the course or courses steered on the way.

Now we shall need a compass and a chart, or, seeing that we are really on land, a large-scale map on which there is a compass rose. A compass rose, by the way, is a circle and pointer showing, usually, both the magnetic North and the true or geographical North. With these two things and our small frame aerial, we can make all necessary calculations to find our position.

For convenience fix a pointer to the base of your portable set, the pointer being at right angles to the frame aerial. Now tune the set to a known station—say, the long-wave transmitter at Droitwich. By rotating the set slowly, find out in which position signals from Droitwich are at their minimum. The pointer you have fixed to the set should then lie parallel to the line along which the waves from Droitwich are travelling.

Now with our compass we can find out what is called the "bearing" of this line— that is, the angle it makes with the magnetic North. All we have to do is to place the compass under the pointer and read off the bearing from the degrees or points round the card. If we have a swinging card compass, so much the better. Otherwise we shall have to turn the compass until the north point on the card is directly under the north point of the needle.

Let us suppose that our pointer shows 30 degrees east of north as the direction in which Droitwich lies from us. Now we turn to the map. At Droitwich mark in the compass directions as shown in Figure 70. Then draw the line AB making an angle of 30 degrees to the east of north. I think you will agree that our position must be *somewhere* on this line, for it is only for places on it that Droitwich has a bearing of 30 degrees east of north. Now tune the set to Radio Paris, and find in what direction signals from it are a minimum. The pointer then gives the direction of Paris—35 degrees south of east, let us say. Turning again to our map, we mark the compass directions at Paris, and draw a line CD making the required angle of 35 degrees south of east. For the same reason as before, our position must be *somewhere* on this line. So our position lies *both* on AB and CD, and there is only one point with just that—the point P, where AB and CD meet. We have thus found the position of your imaginary ship on the map. This point is on dry land, of course, because it is assumed you have been making this trial navigational "fix" in your own room at home, so there is no need to think the artist has made a mistake. If you like, you can trace the map on a piece of thin paper, so that the drawing of the lines will not spoil it. Or another method is to cover the map with cellophane or some such transparent material to receive the drawing.

Position of Ship found by Stations Ashore

Another common method for a ship to use in finding its position at sea requires no apparatus on the ship except the normal wireless transmitter and receiver. The work is actually done by two shore stations. A ship wishing to know its position by this method sends out a wireless request for information. Suppose in Figure 72 that S is the position of the ship. The message is received by land direction-finding station A, which is in communication with land direction-finding station B. Station A tells the ship to transmit signals. This it does, whilst both stations A and B obtain bearings on the ship's transmitter. Suppose station A finds the ship is in the direction 220 degrees as in the drawing, while station B finds its direction

is 290 degrees. B sends its reading to A by telephone and A can then work out the ship's position, because the distance from A to B is known exactly. A gives this information to the ship's captain by wireless, the whole job taking only a few minutes.

Radio Beacons

A most interesting method of guiding the mariner is by means of what are called radio beacons. In the methods previously described it is the *receiving aerial* which is rotated. In the radio beacon it is the *transmitting aerial*. The simplest system possible, and one which again requires no special equipment on the ship, consists of a rotating frame aerial at the shore station turning steadily round at the rate of one revolution per minute. The signal received by the ship will wax and wane according as the shore aerial is end on or broadside on to it. By noting when the signal is a minimum, the ship's wireless operator can determine when the aerial is exactly broadside on to him. Now in addition to the ordinary signal sent out continuously by the transmitter, a special signal is sent out when the aerial points due North. By noting with a stop-watch the time between this special signal and the minimum of the main signal, the operator can determine how long it takes for the aerial to come from its North-South position to one in which it is broadside on to him, and consequently he can deduce the bearing of the station from him. Repeating this for another station, he can calculate his position as we did in Figure 70.

Another system uses an aerial of the beam type, i.e. it sends out a narrow beam of wireless waves akin to a searchlight, and, by rotation of the beam aerial, the beam sweeps round in a circle in a horizontal plane. Short waves of four or five metres are used to produce a very narrow beam

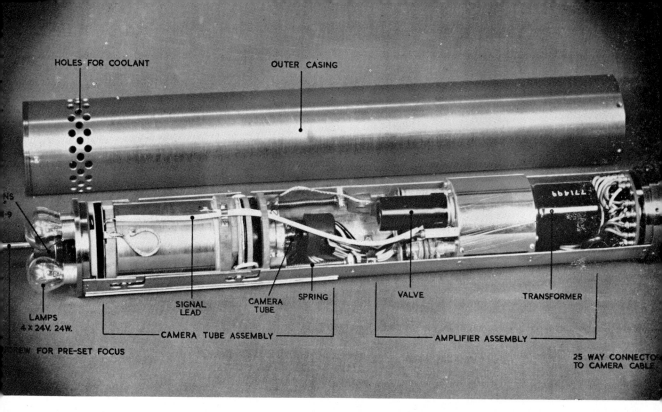

HOLES FOR COOLANT

OUTER CASING

LAMPS
4 × 24V. 24W.

SIGNAL
LEAD

CAMERA
TUBE

SPRING

VALVE

TRANSFORMER

SCREW FOR PRE-SET FOCUS

CAMERA TUBE ASSEMBLY

AMPLIFIER ASSEMBLY

25 WAY CONNECTOR
TO CAMERA CABLE

(Above) *The new television camera under 3″ in diameter which is used for inspection inside the pressure vessel of the atomic reactor at Calder Hall.*

(Below) *The apparatus into which the camera is fitted at Calder Hall.*

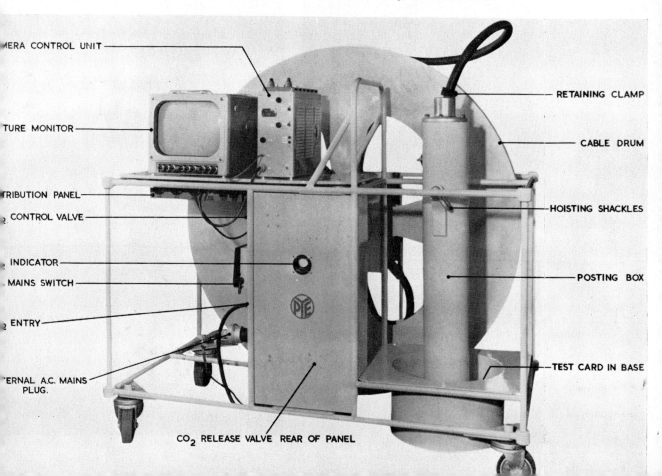

CAMERA CONTROL UNIT

PICTURE MONITOR

DISTRIBUTION PANEL

CONTROL VALVE

INDICATOR

MAINS SWITCH

ENTRY

EXTERNAL A.C. MAINS PLUG.

RETAINING CLAMP

CABLE DRUM

HOISTING SHACKLES

POSTING BOX

TEST CARD IN BASE

CO_2 RELEASE VALVE REAR OF PANEL

Television camera in use in the operating theatre of a hospital.

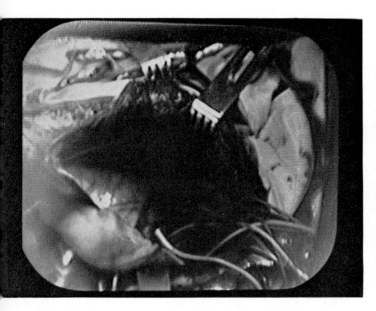

(Above) *Picture from the screen of the monitor during an operation on the heart.* (Right) *A radioactive crystal of the metal zirconium, photographed through a microscope by means of television to see what damage it has suffered by a period of irradiation in an atomic reactor.*

(Top left) *Interior view of an emitron industrial television camera.* (Top right) *"Firestreak", the air to air guided weapon which has an electronic homing device which depends on an infra red, or heat-seeking eye, that steers the missile towards the jet engines of an attacking aircraft.* (Below) *Periscopic television unit installed at Barking Power Station for the remote observation of the interior of a boiler furnace.*

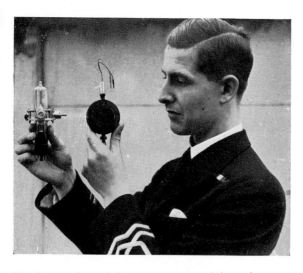

The Sutton tube and the magnetron transmitting valve part of the radar equipment for ships.

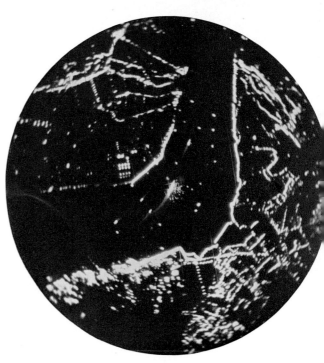

True motion radar; photograph of a radar screen on a ship entering the Lower Hope Reach in the Thames, on its way to Tilbury. The comet-like tails clearly show the motion of the navigator's own ship and of several other vessels nearby. It will be noticed that the ship does not remain in the centre of the screen. It slowly moves until it reaches a point when the operator adjusts the setting. Buildings in the area and a cluster of oil storage tanks can be clearly seen.

P.P.I. photograph of a Decca High Ratio Pulse Radar taken with a scanner fitted on a building on Thames-side adjacent to Hammersmith Bridge. The Metropolitan Water Board Reservoirs can be seen together with many other familiar objects like the quadrangle of St. Paul's School and small suburban houses.

Plan showing the area depicted (on left) on the radar screen.

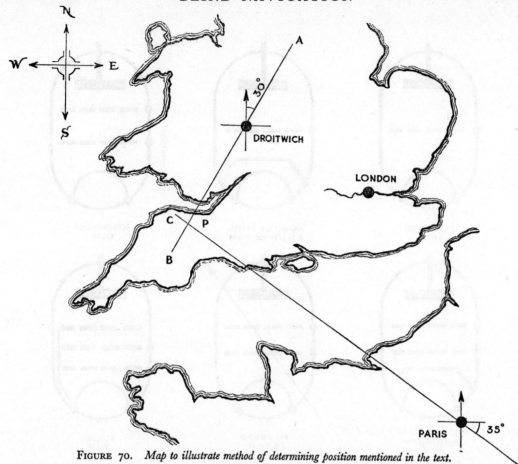

FIGURE 70. *Map to illustrate method of determining position mentioned in the text.*

more easily, so that a ship must be equipped with a short-wave receiver to use the signals, and the working range is short, limiting the system to coastal areas. Each beacon has its distinctive signal, and this is sent out at ever half-point of the compass. Usually the time taken to make one complete revolution, with its sixty-four distinct directional signals, is fixed at two minutes. When a ship wishes to make use of this radio beacon, the operator tunes his short-wave set to the known wave-length of the beacon, and listens for the distinctive directional signals. He picks out the loudest of these, and then from a printed list of directional signals of this particular beacon he obtains the bearing correspond-ing to it, which gives the beacon's bearing. If the same procedure is applied to another beacon, a simple navigational calculation gives the position of the ship.

Homing Devices

A homing device is an arrangement to allow a ship or an aeroplane, but more usually the latter, to follow a path back to a port, airfield or aircraft carrier with the minimum of difficulty. The transmitting aerial at the airfield consists of two fixed frame aerials at right angles, like we used along with the radio-goniometer, but here the two aerials are not set North-South and East-West, but are fixed so that they make equal angles with the track on which we want the plane to come in. The two

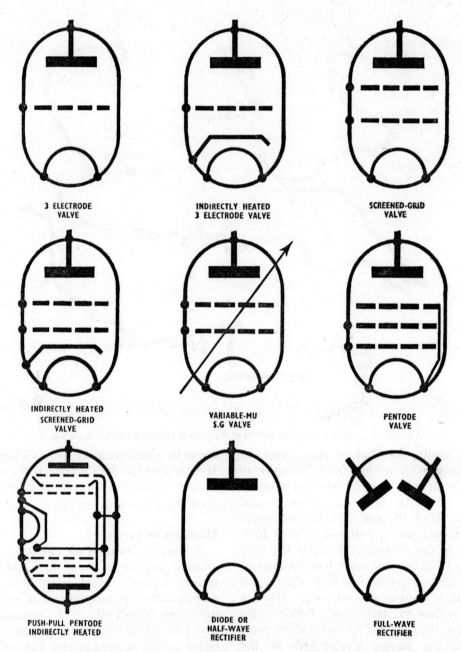

FIGURE 71. *Another selection of symbols as used in radio work. These mainly show valves of various kinds as they are indicated diagrammatically. The method of notation is quite simple. Grids, for example, are shown as dotted lines, filaments as half-circles and anodes as a thick line. One very useful device is the colour code as used on resistances. If you can memorise this code with its various colours, you will be able to read the value of a resistance without figures. Always remember that the spot shows how many O's there are at the end.*

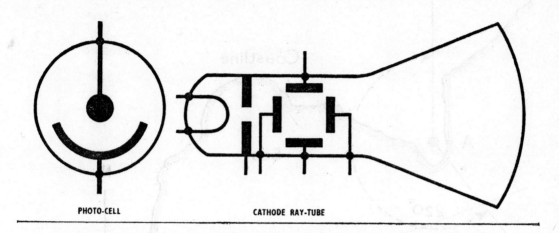

PHOTO-CELL   CATHODE RAY-TUBE

RESISTANCE COLOUR CODE

The first figure of the resistance value is shown by the colour of the body, the second figure by the colour of the tip or end-band; the colour of the spot or centre band shows the number of cyphers. If no spot can be distinguished, it is read as the colour of the body.

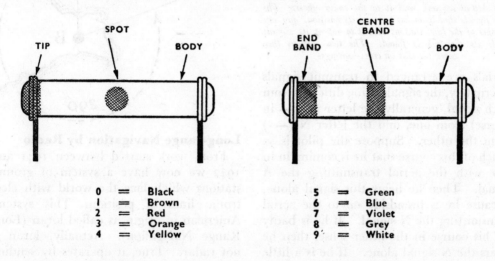

0	=	Black	5	=	Green
1	=	Brown	6	=	Blue
2	=	Red	7	=	Violet
3	=	Orange	8	=	Grey
4	=	Yellow	9	=	White

EXAMPLES: Violet body, green tip, yellow spot - 750,000 ohms.
Brown body, green tip, no spot 1,500,000 ohms.

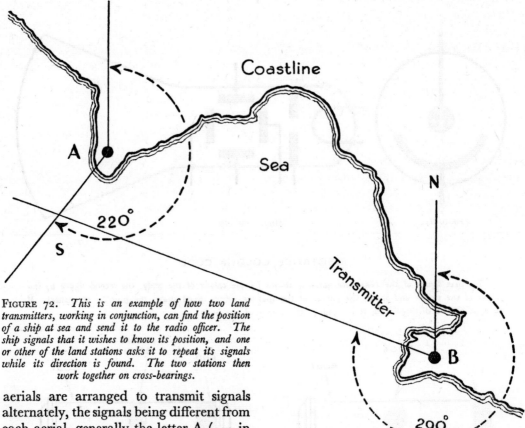

FIGURE 72. *This is an example of how two land transmitters, working in conjunction, can find the position of a ship at sea and send it to the radio officer. The ship signals that it wishes to know its position, and one or other of the land stations asks it to repeat its signals while its direction is found. The two stations then work together on cross-bearings.*

aerials are arranged to transmit signals alternately, the signals being different from each aerial, generally the letter A (· — in Morse) from one, and the letter N (— ·) from the other. Suppose the pilot is so much off his course that he is coming in in line with the aerial transmitting the A signal. Then he hears this signal alone, because he is broadside on to the aerial transmitting the N signal. If he is badly off his course in the other sense, then he hears the N signal alone. If he is a little off the true course he hears one signal louder than the other. When he is exactly on the true course—that is, on a line making equal angles with the two aerials—he hears both signals of equal loudness, and they coalesce to form a continuous dash. To keep right, then, the pilot merely has to hold the plane so that a continuous dash sounds in his headphones —a very simple operation indeed.

Long-range Navigation by Radio

From work started between 1941 and 1942 we now have a system of ground stations which lace the world with electronic lines of position. This system, American in origin, is called loran (Long Range Navigation). Actually, loran is not radar. True, it operates by sending out radio pulses in all directions, but it does not depend on any echo. Put very simply, the idea is as follows: Suppose we have two stations, two or three hundred miles apart, capable of sending out powerful pulses, like those we described in the chapter on radar, and suppose also we have a receiver in the ship or aircraft capable of receiving those pulses. If the pulses from the different stations are distinguishable by some sort of code, then, although a pilot will not be able to tell his actual distance from either by receiving them, he will be able to tell *how much later* the signal from one is received than the other, and from this he will be able to tell how much farther off one is than the other.

Then, with the aid of specially prepared maps, he will be able to tell which of a number of curves he is on, and if he then gets a bearing on a third station he can make another bearing cutting across his first, and thus fix his exact position.

The system as originally operated by the British worked on a short wave-length and was therefore limited to straight-line propagation of the pulses. It was of little use for the navigation of surface vessels—before they are many miles from the ground stations they are over the horizon and out of range.

The American system as now adopted works on a longer wave-length which is not radically different from those used in long-range radio communication. Its waves are the kind that follow the curvature of the earth just in the way that broadcasting waves do. "Fixes" by loran can be taken at distances of several hundred miles—sometimes more than a thousand miles—from the ground stations. Another advantage is that they are independent of weather and visibility.

It is now possible, as a matter of fact, for the navigator, no matter where he may be on the chief sea lanes, to know his exact position from hour to hour, even when the usual methods of navigation by sighting the sun or stars are impossible.

CHAPTER X

SEEING SMALL THINGS

SHORTLY AFTER the War of 1914-18 the whole of Europe was swept by the scourge of a new disease which became popularly known as the "Spanish 'flu". Now most diseases are caused by minute organisms known as "germs", or, to give them their proper name, bacteria.

A great deal was known about the bacteria which caused ordinary diseases from the simple fact that, under the microscope, men could study them and observe their behaviour. But as for the germ which caused the Spanish 'flu, the most powerful microscopes in the world were utterly useless when it came to trying to *see* them, and for many years doctors had a great deal of difficulty in dealing properly with the disease. Later they were to discover that the cause in this case was not a bacterium, but a crystal-like object called a virus.

The same thing has occurred in the plant world. Plants are subject to diseases in just the same way as man; these diseases, in many cases, are also caused by germs. The tobacco plant, for instance, is subject to a disease called "tobacco mosaic", but for a good many years the root cause of the disease defied identification even under the most powerful microscopes that could be made. Here, too, it proved to be a virus.

At the base of the problem of seeing small things lies one fact which we cannot escape. This fact is that *there is a definite limit to the amount by which we can magnify things under the ordinary light microscope.* This limit is bound up with the very

nature of light itself, and before we can understand just how the electron came to man's aid in overcoming this handicap, we ought to make sure that we understand clearly the why and wherefore of "magnification".

We have had occasion to remark before that the last instrument in all processes of "seeing" things is the eye, and that the eye has certain defects. It can hardly be called a "defect"—for in this respect the eye serves all normal purposes admirably—but it is a fact that the average eye cannot distinguish between spots which are *less* than one two-hundred-and-fiftieth of an inch apart. If two ends of a microbe, for instance, are *less* than one two-hundred-and-fiftieth of an inch apart, that microbe will not be seen as a definite object, but only as an indistinct speck. It might be shaped like a ball or like a match for all the human eye could tell.

The task of the microscope, then, is to magnify an object in such a way that the finest detail we want to see appears to be *at least* one two-hundred-and-fiftieth of an inch apart.

It appears, therefore, on the face of it, that all we have to do to magnify to any extent is to use a series of lenses, each of which further magnifies a part of the image already produced by its predecessor; and mechanically this is well within our power nowadays. Nevertheless it is impossible. Why?

The difficulty lies in the fact that, just as it is impossible for the eye to resolve

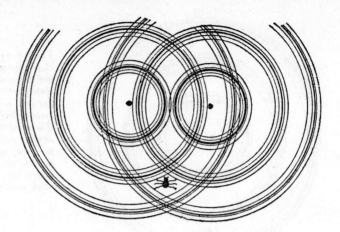

FIGURE 73. *An ordinary microscope cannot be made to magnify an object satisfactorily more than 400 times because light waves are not small enough. Any two points that happen to be less than half the length of a wave apart cannot be seen separately. This drawing of a water beetle on a pond in which two stones have been dropped illustrates the point. The waves created by them strike the water beetle separately, and are consequently distinct—but only because the stones are sufficiently wide apart.*

details less than two hundred and fiftieth of an inch apart, so it is impossible for the best optical instrument to resolve details less than one thousandth part of an inch apart. As far as the eye is concerned, it is just impossible to "see" anything smaller than the size given (two hundred and fiftieth part of an inch), but with the microscope it is a question of the length of the light-waves, because in certain cases these waves tend to get mixed up.

Perhaps this point will bear illustration, so I repeat here one given by a very eminent scientist, Sir George Thompson.

When Two Waves seem like One

Suppose we have an "intelligent water-beetle" on the surface of a pond. A stone is dropped into the pond, the place where it hits becoming the centre of a series of expanding ripples, and from the way the ripples strike the beetle he can tell the direction of the stone. If two stones are dropped at the same time, the beetle will experience a rather irregular motion like that of a sea, but which he would perceive is due to two separate sets of waves coming in two different directions. This is shown in Figure 73. If, however, the stones strike closer together than about the distance between the trough and crest

of a wave, their two wave systems will fuse, and our water-beetle, however intelligent, will think that only one rather large stone has dropped (Figure 74).

Scientists have evolved a general rule about this sort of "interference" as they call it. They say the two interference patterns will be indistinguishable if the spots we are looking at are more than half the wave-length of light apart. Now the light we ordinarily use for microscopy has a half wave-length of about 0·00025 millimetre. To bring two spots 0·00025 of a millimetre apart up to the one two-hundred-and-fiftieth of an inch (one-tenth of a millimetre) we require to see them with the eye, we should require a magnification of 0·1 divided by 0·00025, i.e. 400. It is useless, therefore to magnify anything under the ordinary microscope a great deal beyond this power and expect to see more detail. You can magnify as much more than this as you please. The resulting picture will be easier to read. But the extra magnification is wasted in the sense that nothing *real* can be seen that could not with care be seen without it.

One thing alone, therefore, determines the "power" of a microscope. Here we refer not to "magnifying power", but to

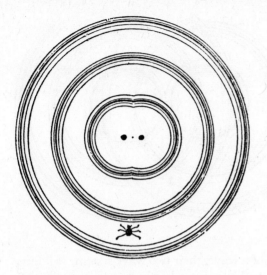

FIGURE 74. *If two stones are dropped into a pond too close together, the separate waves they create are almost indistinguishable. In this drawing it is assumed that the water-beetle is sufficiently intelligent to count up to two, but even so he cannot recognize that there are two waves because they have merged into one before they strike him. The same thing happens with an ordinary microscope when any two dots on the object to be magnified are less than half the length of a light-wave apart. No amount of magnification can result in anything but a blurred image, and that is why the electron microscope, which uses waves so much smaller than those of light, is capable of so much higher powers of magnification.*

what is called "resolving power"—that is, the wave-length of the light used to illuminate the subject.

Using a Different Sort of Light

Suppose, therefore, that we had at our disposal a light which was *shorter* in wave-length than ordinary light, would our microscope have a greater "resolving power"? Certainly. As a matter of fact, when we proceed beyond the violet end of the spectrum (see Figure 19), we find "rays" (although they are visible only through the medium of a photographic plate) which have wave-lengths much shorter than those of visible light.

With these rays we can about double the best magnification previously obtained, but we have not really pushed the limit back very far.

The problem of increasing the power of the ordinary microscope, therefore, and of securing magnifications greater than those obtainable using ultra-violet light, seemed insoluble until a few years ago. About fifteen years ago, however, man called to his aid the electron, and by 1941 a supermicroscope using an electron ray instead of ordinary or ultra-violet light was not

only constructed, but was actually being put on the market in a commercial form.

We can think of the electron in two ways. The obvious way, and the one we have found it most convenient to adopt so far, is to think of it as a tiny particle, incredibly light, but carrying a definite unit charge of electricity—negative electricity. This in all probability is not at all what the electron really is, but if we do think of it in that way certain phenomena are satisfactorily explained, and we can make calculations on this basis, predicting what the electron will do under certain circumstances, and these predictions have so far come out right.

One of the properties of the electron that is satisfactorily explained by this interpretation is its deflection by a magnet or by the magnetic effect exerted by a coil of wire through which a current of electricity flows. Another is its deflection, as we saw in dealing with the cathode ray tube, by a pair of electrically charged plates.

How an Electron Lens is Made

Now, although a beam of electrons would by no means act like a beam of light

(Above) *Radio and radar at sea:* Kronprins Frederik, *a Danish ship with the radar "box" showing clearly on the bridge.* (Left) *A close-up of the same apparatus as that seen on the bridge of the Danish ship.* (Below) *Naval radar set with folding valve cabinet. The mechanic is handling a fluorescent screen of the cathode ray tube.*

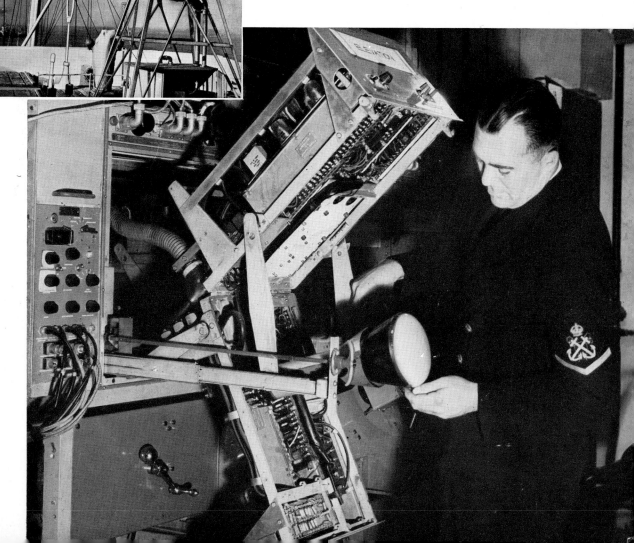

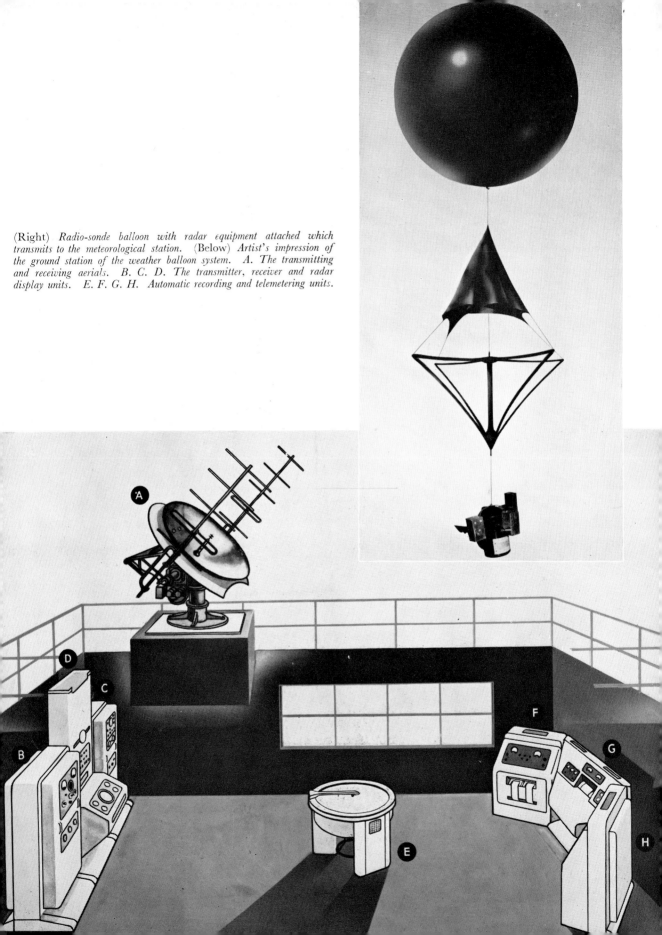

(Right) *Radio-sonde balloon with radar equipment attached which transmits to the meteorological station.* (Below) *Artist's impression of the ground station of the weather balloon system. A. The transmitting and receiving aerials. B. C. D. The transmitter, receiver and radar display units. E. F. G. H. Automatic recording and telemetering units.*

(Above) *The radio receiving and control room of the* Queen Elizabeth.   (Bottom left) *Portpatrick coastal radio station.*

The operator at the Portpatrick transmitter.

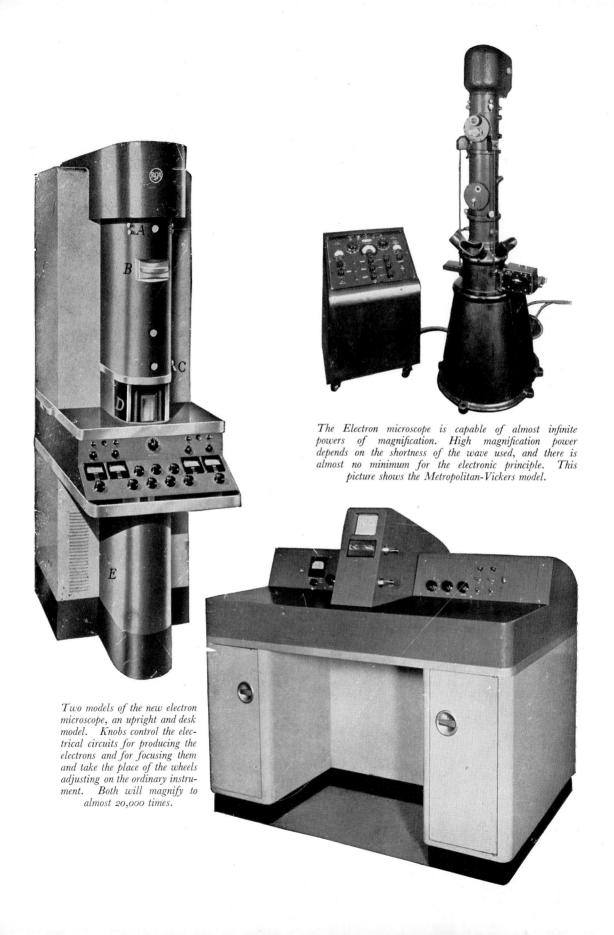

The Electron microscope is capable of almost infinite powers of magnification. High magnification power depends on the shortness of the wave used, and there is almost no minimum for the electronic principle. This picture shows the Metropolitan-Vickers model.

Two models of the new electron microscope, an upright and desk model. Knobs control the electrical circuits for producing the electrons and for focusing them and take the place of the wheels adjusting on the ordinary instrument. Both will magnify to almost 20,000 times.

when it fell on an ordinary glass lens, it *is* possible to construct a "lens" which will act on an electron beam in exactly the same way as an optical lens acts on a beam of light. It is an interesting fact in this connection, although strictly speaking it does not affect us here, that Sir Isaac Newton, probably the greatest scientist the world has ever seen, regarded light—ordinary light—not as a wave-motion in the "ether" as is common today, but as a flight of small "corpuscles" as he called them, and he was able satisfactorily to explain the facts of reflection and refraction by this means, although he did not explain *interference*, which presupposes a wave-nature for light.

However, as we said, it is possible to construct an electro-magnetic lens which will act on a beam of electrons in exactly the same way as an optical lens acts on a beam of light. This lens, shown diagrammatically in Figures 75 and 76, takes the form of a coil of wire wound on a specially-shaped iron core. When a current passes through the wire an intense magnetic field is set up which arranges itself concentrically round the axis of the coil like the hair of a woman's "bun". Electrons taking different paths through this field will naturally be different

amounts. The similarity of the action of an optical lens is shown in Figure 77 (*a*) and (*b*). Lenses using electrostatic deflection, as in a cathode ray tube, may also be used, but they have not proved as effective as the magnetic ones.

Hence there is no insuperable difficulty about constructing an electron counterpart to the ordinary optical microscope. Figure 78 shows the two instruments side by side so that their resemblance, physically, is quite apparent. What about resolving power and magnification?

Two Ways of Thinking about Light

Here you have to take something on trust, but what I told you about Newton and his "corpuscles" should help you to understand what I am getting at. Just as certain phenomena to do with ordinary light, such as reflection and refraction, can be explained if we assume light to consist of a flight of some sort of "corpuscles" which travel in straight lines, whilst other phenomena, such as interference, can only be explained if we assume light to consist of a wave-motion, so certain phenomena with electrons can be explained if we assume they are small, negatively-charged particles, whilst others can only be explained if we think of elec-

FIGURE 75. *Lens of electron microscope. The lens is magnetic in action and controls the stream of electrons like the deflecting plates of the cathode ray tube. A coil of wire is placed in a soft iron frame so that the assembly forms an electro-magnet with a central aperture. It is shown here in section or side-view, with the lines of magnetic force indicated by dotted lines. It is this magnetic field that causes the electrons to "spread out" and so give a magnified view of the object through which they have passed.*

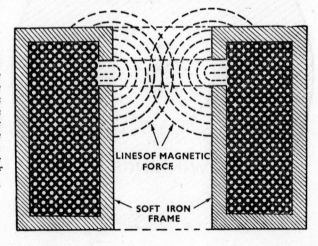

LINES OF MAGNETIC FORCE

SOFT IRON FRAME

trons as a wave-motion—this applies especially to electrons which are travelling fast.

It is a fact, however, that as far as the "power" of the electron microscope is concerned, the electron beam acts as if it were a beam of light—and, what is more, *of light with an incredibly short wave-length.*

Magnifying Power of Electron Microscope

You will see immediately what this means. Whereas the ordinary microscope, using ordinary light, reveals no more useful detail after it has magnified an object 400 times, the electron microscope should enable us to do much better than that, seeing that the wave-length associated with an electron travelling at average speed is about one hundred-thousandth that of visible light. This means that we have at our disposal in the electron microscope wave lengths no more than one two-hundred-millionth of a

millimetre long (0·000000005 mm. against 0·0005 mm. for ordinary light). This implies that we ought to be able to separate spots which are half this distance apart, i.e. no more than one four-hundred-millionth of a millimetre apart. However, owing to certain difficulties with magnetic lenses, this figure has not yet been reached with the electron microscope, but even so a magnification of 50,000 is easily possible—50 times better than that obtainable even with ultra-violet light—and points two millionths of a millimetre apart can be distinguished. Some idea of the tremendous magnifying power that these figures represent will be gained from the statement that under the electron microscope a piece of thin paper held edgewise would appear nine feet thick!

How the Electron Microscope was Developed

The original work on the electron microscope was carried out in the Berlin

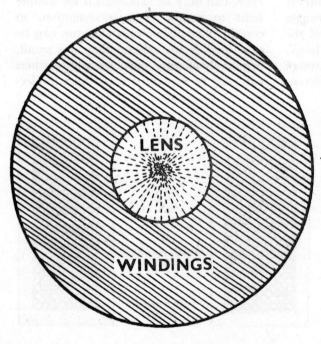

FIGURE 76. *Plan view of magnetic lens. The casing is circular in shape to hold the coil, and has a central aperture in which is created the magnetic field. Through this magnetic field pass the electrons, and according to the power of the field they are "spread out" to give the magnification power required. The electrons cast an enlarged image on a fluorescent screen, and this is photographed for reference by the operator. Owing to the much shorter wave-length possible with the electron principle, the electron microscope is capable of satisfactory magnification powers up to 150,000 diameters.*

Technical High School between 1930 and 1937. It was then first made into a marketable proposition by the great German electrical firm of Siemens-Halske. In 1934, however, a young physicist named Hillier, working in the Toronto University Laboratory, heard a rumour of the new microscope made by the Germans, and immediately set to work, with a small team of helpers and only the resources of the laboratory workshop behind him, to construct a model of his own.

Hillier's instrument surpassed that of the Germans, and was taken up and developed by some of the best brains in the Radio Corporation of America, including the eminent physicist Zworykin, whom we met earlier in connection with the Iconoscope. In 1941, the electron microscope was on the market in America, and six of the instruments came to this country under the Lease-Lend agreement. Commercial models are now in production also in England by Metropolitan-Vickers, and in Holland by Philips. From the photographs it will be seen that the super-microscope is a much bigger and more elaborate affair than the optical microscope with which we are familiar. It has to house, for instance, a great deal of electrical apparatus, together with equipment for pumping out the air so that flight of the electrons will not be hindered.

Principle of Electron Microscope

Its principle is fairly simple to understand if we bear in mind what we have already learned about television.

First, there is a source of electrons. This is similar to the indirectly heated cathode of the valve or cathode ray tube. It includes arrangements for focusing the electrons into a narrow beam. The technique used here again resembles that used in the television set. The electrons thrown off by the cathode are attracted to an anode, which, of course, carries a positive charge, and two things about this are important.

In the first place, the greater the charge the higher the speed with which the electrons are attracted to it, and the shorter the wave-length associated with them. If a low "resolving power" only is needed, the anode need only carry a charge of some 150 volts, and the electrons in this case would have a wave-length of about one five-thousandth that of natural light. If, on the other hand, the charge is raised to 15,000 volts, the electrons would have the very minute wave-length of one hundred-millionth of a millimetre. Modern models work with voltages up to 100,000, but about 60,000 is the usual figure.

Electron Microscope Voltages must not Vary

In the second place, elaborate precautions have to be taken to prevent this voltage *varying* in the slightest degree, for even a small variation has an immediate effect on the *speed* of the electrons. If their speed varies, their wave-length varies, and all the focusing arrangements are upset. Moreover, their power to *penetrate* a specimen depends on their speed, and it it essential that the penetrating power of all the electrons shall be the same or a false picture of the specimen will result. Special electrical circuits keep this voltage right to better than one hundredth of one per cent. Similarly the current in the magnetic lenses must not vary, or the magnification will also change, producing a blurred picture.

As has been said previously, the interior of the instrument must be kept continuously pumped free of air so that the path of the electrons is absolutely unobstructed. However, we have from time to time to change the specimen under observation, and this would normally mean letting the air into our microscope, and a long wait before we could again get it pumped out to the very high vacuum that is required. By fitting an air-lock device, it is possible to change specimens while only letting in a small quantity of air into the space immediately around the specimen-holder, with a consequent wait of only a few minutes before observations can be restarted.

It will already have been noticed from the drawings that the electrons have to pass *through* the specimen with this type of microscope. Now electrons whose speeds have been accelerated by the power of an anode at even 60,000 volts do not possess a great deal of penetrating power. They would hardly get through tissue paper. Beyond this, however, they must get through the specimen without losing speed, or the "lens" will fail to focus them properly.

Thus, at the moment, it is necessary to work with specimens a few millionths of an inch thick. Then, because more electrons get through the thinner parts than get through the thicker ones, the ultimate picture shows a good contrast of light and shade. If all that is wanted is the silhouette of the edges of an object or the picture of holes in an object, then thicker specimens are in order. The solid parts then appear completely black.

Where light and shade are required in a picture taken by the electron microscope, we have to depend on the scattering and absorption of electrons by different parts of the specimen, just as with the ordinary microscope. Those parts which scatter most strongly, like those which absorb most completely, will appear black on the resulting photograph, because the rays will have been scattered somewhere *outside* the aperture of the first lens, and are consequently lost.

Glowing Screen for Electron Microscope

It is quite possible nowadays to make specimens of an almost unbelievable thinness, but the necessity for this imposes a serious handicap on the use of present forms of electron microscope. Another disadvantage is the fact that the bombardment of objects by high-speed electrons sometimes destroys them. Fortunately, bacteria stand up well to this bombardment.

Then there is the disadvantage from a biological point of view that the specimen will be "dead". This prevents us examining the activities of organisms in their natural state. In spite of this, a great amount of useful work has already been done, and technique is steadily improving.

The final image is usually received on a photographic plate, which is affected by electrons in exactly the same way as by light. The images obtained are very sharp, and if a fine-grained photographic plate is used, the resulting picture can usually be enlarged at least tenfold. We can also see and focus the image directly by replacing the plate by a fluorescent screen, which glows when struck by electrons, just like a television screen.

In conclusion, let us see what branches of science and industry benefit from the new service the electron gives to man.

To the scientist and research worker in medicine, biology, bacteriology it will be indispensable. Every laboratory will eventually have to possess an electron microscope, for the instrument will be of first-rate importance in helping them to fight man's worst enemy, disease. In chemistry and metallurgy, too, it will be invaluable, since many of the most important physical and chemical properties of substances are dependent on their shape and size. The following remarks concern some of the most interesting cases where the electron has helped man to "see what had never been seen before".

Viruses Photographed under Electron Microscope

Most interesting, perhaps, is the problem of the viruses, those extremely minute organisms much smaller than bacteria, which, as we have already seen, are the cause of many common diseases in plant and animal. A virus, for instance, is responsible for influenza and probably for the common cold, certainly of poliomyolitus and possibly also of cancer; it is also responsible for many diseases of plants.

In the days before the electron instrument, although some viruses had been identified, the task of determining their properties was very like flying blind over unknown country, but in spite of that many measurements were made, and it was very gratifying to those concerned when the new instrument proved that these measurements were fairly accurate.

One of the first viruses to be photographed under the electron microscope was that of the "tobacco mosaic", as the disease caused by it is called. This is a rod about 300 millionths of a millimetre long. In the purified form the rods show a tendency to join together side by side and end to end. The electron microscope has also been used to study the virus causing disease of the tomato plant, and the influenza virus. The size of the latter has been investigated, and we are

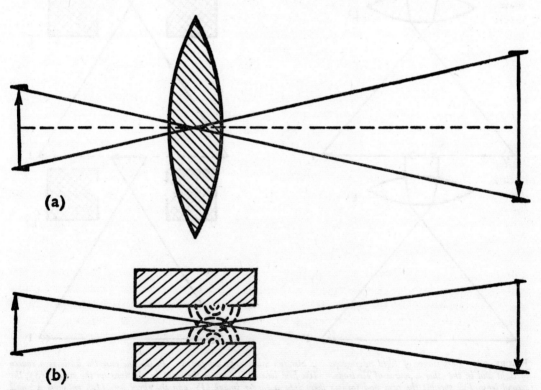

(a)

(b)

FIGURE 77. *Light lens compared with magnetic lens. The principle is the same in each case. The tiny particles that form either waves of light or waves of electronic energy are "spread out" by the lens so that the image they cast is enlarged. Both light waves and electron waves are part of the enormous range of electro-magnetic waves shown in Fig. 19 on page 34.*

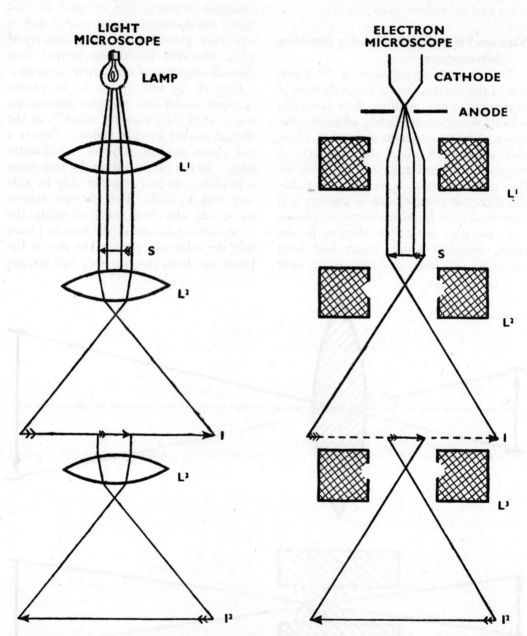

LIGHT
MICROSCOPE

LAMP

L¹

S

L²

I

L³

I²

ELECTRON
MICROSCOPE

CATHODE

ANODE

L¹

S

L²

I

L³

I²

FIGURE 78. *Full stages of light microscope and electron microscope compared. In the one case the basis is a source of light and in the other a source of electrons. The first lens (L₁) focuses the light or electrons on the subject (S), the second lens (L₂) spreads the rays and focuses them into a larger image (I), and the third lens (L₃) enlarges a small section of it (I₂).*

on the way to finding out what it is made of and how it is made up. When we know more about it we should be in a better position to find effective ways of dealing with it.

Electron Microscope and Bacteriophages

One outstanding piece of work accomplished with the electron microscope concerned the tiny, virus-like objects known to the bacteriologist as "bacteriophages"—which make war on bacteria. In effect they are viruses which prey on bacteria, but until recently it was not known how they acted. It was only known that each type of bacteria had its own particular bacteriophage. By applying the electron microscope to the problem, however, a complete solution of the question was obtained.

In conclusion, let us pass to quite a common substance, much used in the manufacture of motor tyres. This substance is carbon black, a species of very finely divided carbon obtained by burning natural gas or oil. The inclusion of carbon black in rubber gives the latter strength and durability far beyond that of natural rubber. The amazing thing about carbon black is the smallness of its particles. These are so fine that they are beyond the range of optical microscopes, and therefore chemists were somewhat at a loss to explain just why they were able to strengthen rubber and enable it to undergo the gruelling conditions imposed on heavy truck tyres and those of, say, racing automobiles.

Some maintained that the particles must be covered with little notches, like the teeth of a saw, but they were unable to check their theories. Others, for different reasons, concluded that they must be relatively smooth. A carbon particle, however, had never been observed with sufficient distinctness to enable a decision to be made.

Mystery of Carbon Black Particles

Then the electron microscope was brought to bear on the problem and the secret of carbon black was immediately revealed. The little particles of this substance were as smooth and round as billiard balls! But not only that: they were *less than half as large* as had previously been thought. This business of size, now, was most important. Many of the most complex processes in industry are governed by what goes on at the "interface"—i.e. the boundary—between two substances, and the larger the area over which the forces at the boundary can exert themselves, the more important they become.

The new value for the surface area of the carbon black particle gave a surface area *per pound* of no less than five million square inches, or over twelve acres! The reinforcing power of carbon black is now thought to lie in the bond established between the surface of the black and that of the rubber.

Thus the electron has completed yet another task in the service of man. It has enabled him to unlock some of Nature's most guarded secrets by extending the range of vision. Few of the ultra-small things of the Universe can now hope to hold their secrets long; only the molecule and the atom still defy the terrific weapons modern science brings to bear in the search for knowledge. Even now the bigger molecules—the so-called "chain" molecules or "polymers"—are yielding to the assault. Before long it may be that we shall be able to see a molecule of starch, cellulose or sugar!